ACCELERATORS

ROBERT R. WILSON, professor of physics and director of the Laboratory for Nuclear Studies at Cornell, was born in Franklin, Wyoming, in 1914. Educated at the University of California at Berkeley (A.B. 1936, Ph.D. 1940), he studied under the late Nobel Prize winner Dr. Ernest O. Lawrence and was involved in the exciting early work done on the cyclotron. While still at graduate school, Wilson began his research on the scattering of protons by protons, a subject that was to concern him until 1946.

After receiving his Ph.D., Dr. Wilson went to Princeton as an instructor and was soon engaged in some of the early measurements of the neutron-absorbing properties of U 235. In the fall of 1941, he invented the scheme for separating the isotopes of uranium called the "Isotron" method. Receiving considerable financial and technological support for the development of this method, Wilson was placed in charge of an atomic energy project at Princeton composed of fifty people.

In 1943, after the Princeton project was abandoned, the group moved en masse to Los Alamos with Wilson as director of the cyclotron group. The following year, he became the head of the Experimental Nuclear Physics Division and held this position until 1945, when he left Los Alamos after accepting an associate-professorship at Harvard.

Very shortly after arriving in Cambridge, Dr. Wilson was invited to Cornell University as director of the Laboratory of Nuclear Studies. At the end of the fall term (1946), he left Harvard to assume his present position.

RAPHAEL LITTAUER was born in Leipzig, Germany, in 1925, and moved to England in 1939. Winning the Major Open Scholarship, he attended Christ College, Cambridge University, from 1943 to 1950. In 1950, after receiving his

Ph.D., Dr. Littauer came to the United States and assumed his duties as a research associate at Cornell University.

Except for 1954–55, when he was associated with the General Electric Research Laboratory in Schenectady, Dr. Littauer has worked on accelerators with Dr. Wilson at Cornell. In 1955, he was appointed a research associate professor.

ACCELERATORS

Machines of Nuclear Physics

by Robert R. Wilson
and Raphael Littauer

SCIENCE
STUDY
SERIES
Ⓞ

Published by Anchor Books
Doubleday & Company, Inc.
Garden City, New York
1960

Available to secondary school
students and teachers through
Wesleyan University Press Incorporated
Columbus 16, Ohio

ILLUSTRATIONS BY BURT MADER

ACKNOWLEDGMENTS

Photographs were reprinted through the courtesy of the following:

Plate I: Massachusetts Institute of Technology.

Plate II: *Proceedings of the Royal Society,* A Vol. 134.

Plate III: Cavendish Laboratory, Cambridge, England.

Plates IV and X: Laboratory of Nuclear Science, Massachusetts Institute of Technology.

Plate V: High Energy Physics Laboratory, Stanford University.

Plates VI, VII, VIII, IX, XII, and XIV: University of California Lawrence Radiation Laboratory.

Plate XI: Laboratory of Nuclear Studies, Cornell University.

Plate XIII: Brookhaven National Laboratory.

Plates XV and XVI: Dr. Georg Gerster—Black Star.

THE SCIENCE STUDY SERIES

The Science Study Series offers to students and to the general public the writing of distinguished authors on the most stirring and fundamental topics of physics, from the smallest known particles to the whole universe. Some of the books tell of the role of physics in the world of man, his technology and civilization. Others are biographical in nature, telling the fascinating stories of the great discoverers and their discoveries. All the authors have been selected both for expertness in the fields they discuss and for ability to communicate their special knowledge and their own views in an interesting way. The primary purpose of these books is to provide a survey of physics within the grasp of the young student or the layman. Many of the books, it is hoped, will encourage the reader to make his own investigations of natural phenomena.

These books are published as part of a fresh approach to the teaching and study of physics. At the Massachusetts Institute of Technology during 1956 a group of physicists, high school teachers, journalists, apparatus designers, film producers, and other specialists organized the Physical Science Study Committee, now operating as a part of Educational Services Incorporated,

Watertown, Massachusetts. They pooled their knowledge and experience toward the design and creation of aids to the learning of physics. Initially their effort was supported by the National Science Foundation, which has continued to aid the program. The Ford Foundation, the Fund for the Advancement of Education, and the Alfred P. Sloan Foundation have also given support. The Committee is creating a textbook, an extensive film series, a laboratory guide, especially designed apparatus, and a teacher's source book for a new integrated secondary school physics program which is undergoing continuous evaluation with secondary school teachers.

The Series is guided by a Board of Editors consisting of Paul F. Brandwein, the Conservation Foundation and Harcourt, Brace and Company; John H. Durston, Educational Services Incorporated; Francis L. Friedman, Massachusetts Institute of Technology; Samuel A. Goudsmit, Brookhaven National Laboratory; Bruce F. Kingsbury, Educational Services Incorporated; Philippe LeCorbeiller, Harvard University; and Gerard Piel, *Scientific American.*

CONTENTS

THE SCIENCE STUDY SERIES   7
PREFACE   11
INTRODUCTION   17

1. THE NEED FOR HIGH ENERGY   21
   Waves and Images—The Electron Micro-
   scope — Scattering Experiments — Creating
   Particles—Equivalence of Mass and Energy

2. THE FIRST ACCELERATOR   35
   Accelerating Electrons—Roentgen's Radia-
   tion—The Energy of X-Rays—High Voltages
   —X-Rays in Research

3. THE EARLY MACHINES: DIRECT
   ACCELERATORS   49
   Rutherford's Examination of the Atom—
   The Cockroft-Walton Machine—Van de
   Graaff's Electrostatic Generator

4. LINEAR ACCELERATORS   69
   A Mechanical Analog—Automatic Timing
   Stability — Linac Design — Crowding the
   Speed Limit

5. THE CYCLOTRON   87
   Particles in Spiral Orbits—Phase and Frequency—Energy Limits of the Cyclotron—Lawrence and the California Radiation Lab

6. THE BETATRON   103
   Electrons in Circular Orbits—Two Magnetic Fields—Injection and Extraction—From Electrons to X-Rays—Focusing and Orbital Stability

7. THE ELECTRON SYNCHROTRON   117
   Traffic Problems—Policing the Particles—New Machines for New Physics

8. THE SYNCHRO-CYCLOTRON   129
   Skirting the Relativistic Barrier—Beams of Mesons

9. THE PROTON SYNCHROTRON   137
   Anti-matter—The Cosmotron and the Bevatron—Speculations

10. FOCUSING   143
   Acceptance of a Pipe—Alternating-Gradient Focusing—To Greater Intensity

11. SYNCHROCLASH   157
   Solution by Head-on Collision—Improving the Odds

12. COSMIC ACCELERATORS   163
   The Origin of Cosmic Radiation—Collision with Plasmoids

CONCLUSION   167
APPENDICES   171
BIBLIOGRAPHY   187
INDEX   189

PREFACE

Now and again through history something has happened to a particular man to give him a vision of the future. It happened to Columbus, and we are all familiar with what a nuisance he made of himself until the Queen of Spain allowed him to fulfill his vision of sailing across the Atlantic. It happened to the builders of the great Gothic cathedrals of twelfth- and thirteenth-century France, and their visions of structural perfection left monuments as inspiring to us as they were to the architects. In our own day it happened to a young man from South Dakota, Ernest Orlando Lawrence. His vision combined discovery and technological achievement. He dreamed of building mighty nuclear machines that would probe the secrets of the atom as huge telescopes had probed the heavens.

Like many single-minded men, Lawrence dwelled on his vision until it became an obsession. His life was dedicated to fulfillment of his dream: he worked with his hands, with his mind, and with his intuition; he invented, he financed, he administered. He lived to see the vision realized; in laboratories all over the world men accepted it and carried it forward.

In a sense this book is a description of the Lawrence

dream and its fulfillment. Such a statement is an exaggeration, of course, for the science of high-energy nuclear physics has had many roots. Even the part of it most intimately associated with Lawrence—particle accelerators—grew from the inspired efforts of hundreds of physicists, each with his own vision. But it is human to choose the first and the most dramatic man and to emphasize his style and contribution when you seek unity in the development of an idea, a cathedral, or a machine.

In Lawrence we meet again the happy American success story. He came from the heart of a still raw land where the frontier times were only yesterday. He was fortunate in his schooling; at the University of South Dakota he met a professor, L. E. Akeley, who stimulated his interest in physics. Like most American physicists, he studied at several universities—Minnesota, Chicago, and then at Yale, where he received the Ph.D. degree in 1925. Very early in his career he showed himself to be an intrepid experimenter and inventor; when at Yale, he devised a color-television process, and in later life he developed a workable color set. He perfected a method of measuring time intervals as short as a few billionths of a second, and he showed that photoelectrons were emitted in this almost infinitesimal time.

As a young professor of physics at the University of California, Lawrence became interested in the problem of accelerating ions. (An ion, you will recall, is an atom that has departed from its electrically neutral state either by adding an electron and becoming negative or by losing an electron and becoming positive.) One day while he was reading in the library, he chanced on an article in a German publication on this subject. The article discussed a particular method of accelerating ions which kindled his imagination, and within minutes he had formulated his own approach to the problem—no less than the principle of the cyclotron! It was an invention that was to dominate the development of nuclear physics.

Now obviously it is one thing to conceive a device and something else again to make it work in a practical way. Before Lawrence's cyclotron actually accelerated particles, he and his students had to lay the groundwork for entirely new engineering techniques concerning high vacuums, radio oscillators, and electronics. Five years had passed, and he had become a full professor at the age of twenty-nine, before he and his team achieved success.

In 1932 a small cyclotron they had built gave a beam of protons at an energy of 1.2 million electron volts—until then the highest energy ever produced. But it was not enough just to produce high-speed protons. For some years it had been known, from the research of Ernest Rutherford in England and from the development of wave mechanics, that protons of about this energy, or perhaps even less, would disintegrate the nucleus of the atom, and several laboratories were racing to be the first to do it. In one particularly unfortunate and dramatic attempt, an insulated cable was strung between Mount Genevosa in the Alps and its neighboring peak, and potentials as high as 15 million volts were observed on the cable in storms. Playing with such a force is dangerous business. When they tried to apply this voltage across an ion-acceleration tube, one of the experimenters, Dr. C. Urban, was electrocuted.

Eventually the distinction of being the first to disintegrate a nucleus artificially went to J. D. Cockroft and E. T. S. Walton at the famous Cavendish Laboratory, at Cambridge, England. They were not particularly successful at getting a high voltage—they did get to 0.7 Mv (million volts), although they had trouble holding it on their accelerator tube—but they decided to make a try at the experiment anyway. At Cavendish there was a wealth of experimental apparatus such as particle counters, and, better still, there existed a magnificent tradition of doing extremely clever and extremely simple experiments—the Rutherford tradition.* Thus, although Lawrence produced protons of the necessary energy before Cockroft and Walton, he lacked a laboratory versed in the techniques of nuclear physics, and he lost the race to cleverer experimenters using more modest methods. Taking the lesson to heart, he gathered a group of first-class men and organized the Radiation Laboratory of the University of California at Berkeley, which in time became the world's leading laboratory of nuclear physics.

Students and physicists came from all over the world to work with Lawrence. They built a succession of cyclotrons, each several times larger than the one before. The mighty 10,000-ton Bevatron, which is nearly 150 feet in diameter and today gives protons at an energy of 6 billion electron volts, is the culmination of the series. Each step in the construction of more powerful machines leads to ever more powerful tools of nuclear exploration. The laboratory attained its full scientific maturity in the 1950s, when mesons were artificially created and their properties brilliantly investigated. It was at this laboratory that the first anti-proton was observed, the first glimpse into the mysterious world of anti-matter.

Lawrence's personality was infectious. He was hardworking, always optimistic, and determined that no obstacle should ever stop him. The men who worked with him and others who came afterward caught something of his spirit, and a style of physics, sometimes called

* See *The Restless Atom*, by Alfred Romer (Science Study Series).

"Berkeleyitis" by those who don't like it, grew up at the Radiation Laboratory. The Berkeley style perhaps is best described by the words "can do." It is an enthusiastic and occasionally arrogant attitude that proclaims that almost anything is possible. Practical, even theoretical, difficulties are often ignored. In the solution of a technical problem no resource, human, financial, or scientific, is left untapped. The infection has spread to nuclear researchers around the world and, combined with the Rutherford tradition, it helps to explain, in some measure at least, the almost miraculous development of nuclear physics and the discoveries of the nature of elementary particles. To tell the whole story it is necessary to discuss Niels Bohr, Werner Heisenberg, Enrico Fermi, and many others, but we shall concern ourselves here with the part of nuclear physics that involves particle accelerators and thus stems from the vision of Ernest Orlando Lawrence.

INTRODUCTION

A high-energy particle accelerator is about as specialized as a tool can be, and you might ask why anyone would devote a whole book to a few specialized tools, even if some of them are monstrously large and hideously expensive. Why not leave the tools to lab manuals and get on with fundamental discoveries? Ordinarily this would be a reasonable attitude, but there is nothing ordinary about accelerators.

In the first place, there is a great thrill to be had from building a big accelerator and a great sense of achievement from making one work. Lore and legend surround these machines, and they generate competition between physicists. The atmosphere about them carries the same excitement you find at the start of a championship sports-car or speedboat race or, closer still, at the launching of a rocket for space exploration. With the successful operation of a new accelerator, there is the tremendous satisfaction of having solved intricate technological problems; and how much sweeter still is the satisfaction of reaping a rich harvest of scientific discoveries! Think of the rocket designer's thrill when his "baby" soars off to regions never reached before!

Where the rocket man builds ever more powerful engines to give his birds longer reach and greater payload, the accelerator man strives for ever higher energies for his particles. But another record just for the sake of the record itself is not what either scientist seeks. The purposes of the tools supply the motivations of the designers. The rocketeer wants to know what is happening 'way out there in space. At the other extreme, the accelerator man wants to probe deeper and deeper into the ultimate mystery of matter. He wants to know the basic structure of atoms, of their nuclei, and of the strange particles of which they are composed. The rocket man makes tools to reach inconceivable distances; the nuclear physicist makes tools to penetrate the unimaginably small. And his tools are quite as fascinating and spectacular as the flaming, roaring space rocket.

This book, then, will talk about accelerators, how they were developed, how they have achieved higher and higher energies. Discoveries stimulated the design and construction of new machines; the new machines produced further discoveries. Useless to try to draw a line between tool and job—each has led to the other. Most of the men involved in construction of accelerators have been able later to exploit their own tools for research. In this they are like the racing-car designer who pilots his own car on the speedway; there is a double satisfaction. To give you some sense of it is the purpose of this book. It will take you into many fields of physics and engineering—from atomic fundamentals to production of high vacuums, electromagnetism, high-voltage engineering, pulse electronics, and Relativity. This is a lot of ground to cover, and you will begin to see why it will take a whole book to survey what may have seemed to be a hopelessly specialized subject.

ACCELERATORS

Chapter 1

THE NEED FOR HIGH ENERGY

Let us begin by thinking for a bit about the act we call seeing. This may seem far afield from accelerators, but if you will bear with us, you will understand why we choose this beginning. You know, of course, that you see when light from some object passes through the lens of your eye and falls on the light-sensitive nerve cells of the retina. Are you seeing an actor when he appears on your TV screen in a "live" performance? Is it seeing when you look at a ship through a telescope? And when you notice a bright blue spot in the sky, are you really "seeing" the Dog Star, Sirius, whose light has taken eight and a half years to get here?

A little reflection will convince you that there is more to this word "seeing" than a quick look at the dictionary might suggest. Seeing can mean seeing things, or it can mean seeing things with artificial aids, or it can mean seeing the *effects* of things.

Now the ultimate purpose of all work with accelerators is to "see" atoms. Some people are perfectly content when you have told them that their houses, the earth, and the stars are made of atoms. Others want to look further. With a magnifying glass they can see the fibers of the cloth in their clothes; with a microscope

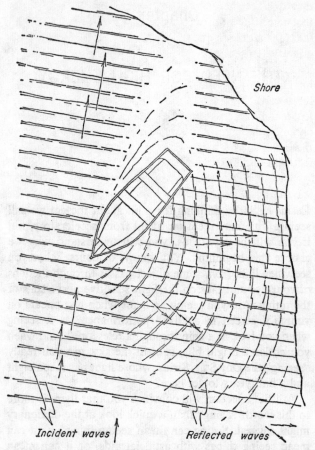

Incident waves   *Reflected waves*

FIG. 1. *The rowboat reflects the incident waves in a pattern that would tell an observer at a distance that the incident waves were striking something. In theory, at least, the observer could learn to deduce the shape of the boat from the pattern of the reflected waves.*

they can see the cells of the fibers. But the large cells that can be seen through a microscope still have 1,000,-000,000 atoms in them. No matter how carefully you grind the lenses of the microscope, no matter how many lenses you may use or how strong you make them, no human eye by this means will ever see things smaller than those cells. This limitation is not merely one of imperfect technique: it is a much stronger sort of impossibility, based on the process of seeing. If you wish to see atoms, then, you will need altogether different kinds of aids. Let us try to understand why.

To be visible, objects must reflect, or *scatter,* the light waves that strike them. You can think of a comparable situation that will help you to understand. Imagine a rowboat floating on a lake, as sketched in Fig. 1. There are small ripples in the water traveling in a well-defined pattern toward the boat. The boat will deflect these ripples, and if you study the way in which the ripples are reflected, you can deduce the presence of the boat. With a little practice, indeed, you could even get some information about the precise shape of the boat. In other words, you would be *seeing* the boat with the aid of the ripples. Similarly, you could learn something about the boat if you were in the "shadow" behind it.

Waves and Images

Now imagine the same boat in a storm with large waves. Clearly the boat will not disturb the waves much. Even if it should deflect the waves a little, you would not be able to deduce the exact position or the shape of the boat; the waves are so "coarse" that it is impossible to deduce any detail with their help. So, we have here an illustration of our first principle: If you want to observe fine details, you must use waves whose wavelength (distance from crest to crest or trough to trough) is no larger than the size of the object you are trying to see.

It is because our eyes respond only to certain wavelengths of light that we must accept a lower limit on the size of what we actually can see. But visible light is only a part of the radiation that vibrates through the universe as wave motion with the same speed as light. There are long radio waves and short radio waves, infrared and ultraviolet light, X-rays and gamma rays. All these vibrations of the same general character and the same velocity of light, taken together, are known as the *electromagnetic spectrum*. The wavelengths range from about 10^6 (a one followed by six zeros) centimeters for the longest radio waves to about 10^{-14} (one, divided by one followed by fourteen zeros) centimeter and even less for the shortest gamma rays.* The wavelength of visible light ranges from about 3.5×10^{-5} cm to 7.5×10^{-5} cm, which, as you can see, includes a very small portion of the entire electromagnetic spectrum.

Since nature prevents us from directly observing finer details than the fiber cells we have mentioned, we cannot restrict ourselves to visible light if we want to examine smaller objects. But objects do reflect, or scatter, shorter-wavelength radiation. With appropriate apparatus interposed between our eyes and the objects, and with our definition of "seeing" enlarged and extended beyond the dictionary's definition so that we can use these shorter wavelengths, then we can "see" almost inconceivably small things.

We can use ultraviolet rays, for example, in a microscope. True, our eyes will not see ultraviolet, and therefore we must have an intermediate stage. Our apparatus records the image on a fluorescent screen or photographic film, which interacts with ultraviolet light. Then

---

* If you are not familiar with this way of expressing magnitudes, Appendix II explains it.

on the screen or film we "see" the tiny object. X-rays and gamma rays, having still shorter wavelengths, would enable us to see still smaller objects, but since the lenses of an ordinary microscope no longer work —that is, refract—for such short wavelengths, a different apparatus must be used.

The Electron Microscope

The electron, one of the fundamental particles of the atom, also has wave properties; hence it can be used for seeing. The electron microscope is a standard tool in a well-equipped laboratory today, and you no doubt have seen its pictures of virus molecules and other impressively small things. In the electron microscope, properly designed magnets take the place of the lenses in ordinary microscopes. Electrons are charged particles, and charged particles are deflected when they pass through a magnetic field. Just as a lens can focus light by deflecting the beam, so can a magnetic field focus an electron beam by deflecting it.

You will notice that we have spoken of the electron as a *particle* and in the same breath said that it has *wave* properties. How can this be? It seems contradictory. How can a particle of matter behave like a wave? The answer lies in the fact that the concepts *particle* and *wave* are taken from everyday experience and cannot be transferred unchanged into the realm of the atom. We use these words for lack of better ones, since our imagination has to have some form of crutch. This does not, however, make it legitimate to draw too precise conclusions from our rough mental pictures. The only way to stay on firm ground is to stick to the experimental observations themselves, and here the dual nature turns out to be quite orderly. If your apparatus is sensitive to the particle aspect of electrons—say it is a Geiger

counter, which gives a definite click for each event that
stimulates it—then you will detect electrons as particles.
If, on the other hand, you perform an experiment sensitive to the wave aspects of electrons—for example by
looking at the ripple-like patterns that they will make in
moving around an obstacle—then the electrons will dis-
play their wave nature for you. It all depends on how
you look at them! Actually, a quite precise way of stating the situation is this: Electrons move through space
like waves, but when made to interact with a detector,
they will behave like particles.

The electron's wave characteristics, and especially the
wavelength, interest us here in our efforts to "see" things
as small as the other subatomic particles. The wavelength depends upon how fast the electron is moving
—the faster it moves, the shorter the wavelength becomes. This makes the electron a convenient seeing aid,
for we can adjust the speed, hence wavelength, to the
size of the object we want to observe.

The electron microscope can reveal details many
times smaller than can be observed with visible light. As
we have said, this instrument was modeled on the construction of the optical microscope, and it does produce
an actual image except that the image is upon a fluorescent screen or a photographic plate. Its lens system gath-
ers up electrons diverging from a certain point and brings
them together again—*focuses* them—to form the image,
just as the optical lens works with light rays. The electron lens can be a suitable set of electrodes that attract
or repel the electrons, urging them into the desired path,
or it can be a carefully controlled magnetic field. If we
accelerate the electron with about two kilovolts, which
is a typical voltage used in some electron microscopes,
its wavelength becomes about 3×10^{-9} cm. Compare
this with the wavelengths of visible light—that is, several
times 10^{-5} cm—and recall that the shorter the wave-

length the finer the detail revealed. It then becomes obvious why the electron microscope is 10,000 times more powerful than the optical microscope and why we need even higher-energy accelerators in the study of still smaller structures.

As we have pointed out, seeing is not all that it seems to be. In telescopes and microscopes we see a sharply defined image with a recognizable shape. When things are very small compared with the wavelength of the light shining on them, we cannot see a clear image, but we certainly can tell that something is present. The object scatters the light. No matter how carefully we focus, we may not be able to make out the exact shape, but we still can infer several things. We can measure how much light is scattered in specific directions and how much is transmitted through the object; in this way we can get *some* information about the shape and physical properties.

We can extend this scattering information if we change the energy or speed of the particles, or change the particles themselves. The electrically charged electron will give different information from that of a neutral particle such as a neutron.*

As we proceed from the study of the atom to the study of subatomic matter—the nucleus, for example—we need higher energies than those for which we can construct a lens system. Then we must forgo an actual image of what we are observing and make do with what we can learn from the scattered particles. Such a process of interpretation is much less direct. Now we are "seeing" the nucleus by deducing its properties from the patterns of scattering.

* See *The Neutron Story*, by Donald J. Hughes (Science Study Series).

Scattering Experiments

In a typical experiment (Fig. 2) a beam of extremely energetic electrons strikes the substance under investigation—here hydrogen, which is the simplest atom, with the simplest nucleus, one proton. The energy of the electrons might be as much as one billion electron volts—that is, they have been accelerated by a voltage of one billion volts—and at this energy their wavelength is only about 10^{-13} cm. The hydrogen nuclei scatter the electrons as suggested in the diagram. The apparatus in-

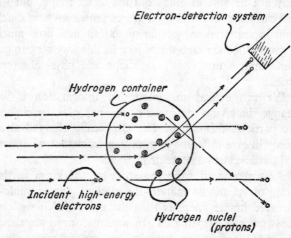

FIG. 2. *The technique of "seeing" hydrogen nuclei with high-energy electrons is similar, as this simplified diagram suggests, to the technique of "seeing" the boat of Fig. 1 with water waves. The number of scattered electrons counted when the detection system is moved to various positions gives information about the nuclei which cause the scattering. The experimenter does not see an image, but he can measure the electron scattering and make deductions from it.*

cludes a complex system of magnetic analyzer and scintillation counters to detect the deflected electrons but not those involved in more complicated interactions. When we measure the numbers of scattered electrons at different positions of the detector system, we can deduce some vital information about the structure of the proton.

Now this, obviously, is an involved and indirect process, but we do obtain information that is just as valuable as if it had appeared as a neat, sharp image on a photographic plate. It is possible, for example, to calculate the diameter of the proton (about 3×10^{-13} cm) and to deduce whether electric charge is uniformly distributed on it. (It is not.) The smallness of the diameter tells you immediately why we had to use such high-energy, short-wavelength electrons.

When choosing a particle to accelerate in these experiments, we have to consider more than wavelength. The particles must be such that the material under examination will scatter them suitably. Try, for example, to see clear glass marbles in a glass of water! You will run into difficulties, but not because the marbles are too small for the wavelength of visible light. It is because they are *transparent* to the light and, especially when they are immersed in water, do not scatter much of it. Paint the marbles black and you will have no trouble seeing them. On the other hand, the clear marbles might be quite visible in an X-ray picture—they absorb X-rays more readily than water does.

So, we must have just the right kind of interaction between the radiation and the material we want to investigate. Indeed, what we see will depend on what the interaction is. When the high-energy electron beam struck the hydrogen, the interaction was a simple electrical one: the positive protons attracted the negative electrons and so deflected the beam. What we actually were measuring was the *electric* radius of the proton, that is, the distribution of electric charge on it.

If we had used other particles, we would have obtained a different set of factors. Suppose, for example, we bombarded the hydrogen with high-energy protons. Quite apart from the electrical forces involved, there would be a strong interaction of the radiation, composed of protons, and the "target" material, also protons, because protons exert a mysterious force on each other. In this case we can say we are also seeing the *nuclear* aspect of the proton in addition to its electrical aspects. The nuclear force, which has been extensively studied in just such experiments, is what binds together the more complicated nuclei of the heavier elements. An understanding of its nature is vital to nuclear physics.

All this seems to have carried us a long way from the simple process of seeing. There is really little difference. Indirect and complicated as the experimental techniques do become, fundamentally the process is the same as ordinary vision. We shine suitable radiation on an object, and we see how much of it is scattered and where. High-energy accelerators play a unique part in the process as we search for finer and finer detail; but their usefulness does not stop there. Some of the most dramatic and fundamental discoveries of modern physics have resulted from another function of the accelerator.

Creating Particles

Sometimes, in the interaction of our bombarding particles and the target material, entirely new particles suddenly appear. This is a thrilling business. In the laboratory we are duplicating some of the processes that must surely be occurring in the universe about us and in the upper reaches of the earth's atmosphere, where cosmic rays come within our observation.

The origin of these cosmic rays is not yet understood. Some of them come from the sun, some from regions of space very much farther away. They are high-energy particles, mostly protons, and they rain upon the earth constantly. Day and night, year after year, with little change of intensity, this flux of high-energy radiation keeps arriving. The total number of particles is not so very large; it often takes a long period of observation to detect a particular cosmic-ray event.

Cosmic rays interact violently with atoms in our atmosphere and in the process give rise to new particles. Sometimes these new particles penetrate the atmosphere to the surface of the earth, and we can observe them directly. Sometimes they disintegrate quickly far above the earth. Then we must seek the disintegrations where they take place; we send up balloons and rockets to "catch" them.

We have made many discoveries with the help of cosmic rays, but scientists are never satisfied. The scientist wants to exert control over the processes he studies so he can ask questions and find answers. Thus it has been with the new particles. Investigators observed them first in the cosmic-ray interactions. Now in the laboratory, using accelerators, we can duplicate some of the processes and study them.

When you talk of creating a new particle, or new particles, you at once open the door to an urgent question. How can you create something that has mass? How can you make material from nothing?

Equivalence of Mass and Energy

To resolve this paradox, we must turn to one of the conclusions of Albert Einstein's Theory of Relativity. Einstein deduced a complete equivalence of *mass* and *energy;* he asserted, in fact, that the two are merely different manifestations of one and the same phenomenon: $E = mc^2$, where E is energy, m is the equivalent mass, and c the speed of light, approximately 300,000 kilometers a second, or 186,000 miles per second.

Einstein's equation seemed hard to swallow when he first announced it, but it ties in beautifully with the rest of the Relativity Theory, which is no less daring. Remember, too, that Einstein did not come on his discovery by chance. He formulated it to explain certain startling observations, and it explained them so well that there can be little doubt that it is a correct and useful theory. So scientists had to reorient their thinking and try to absorb Einstein's ideas into the way they imagined and described the physical world.

Let us consider some examples in which it becomes clear that mass and energy are equivalent. Painstaking measurements have shown that when light from distant stars passes close to the sun, the light is deflected slightly. Just as a bullet would be attracted to the sun, so is the light attracted and its path therefore bent slightly. Light, which has an energy associated with it, also has mass, a fact to be expected from the Theory of Relativity.

The most *spectacular* example of exchanging mass and energy in measurable amounts came in the explosion of atomic bombs, where part of the mass of the

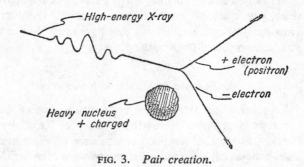

FIG. 3.   *Pair creation.*

uranium nuclei is used up in the nuclear reaction and released in the form of enormous amounts of energy. However, the purest demonstration of all is in the effect known as *pair creation,* illustrated in Fig. 3. A high-energy X-ray passes close to a heavy nucleus. In the strong electric field of the charged nucleus, the X-ray suddenly disappears, and in its place two electrons are created! One electron, called a positron, is electrically positive; the other is the more common negative kind. Energy in the form of an X-ray has changed into mass in the form of the two electrons, a striking example of the conversion of energy into mass.

The reverse of pair creation happens quite readily, too. When a positive electron meets a negative one, the two *annihilate* each other and release their mass-energy in the form of X-rays (Fig. 4). The process explains why under ordinary conditions positive electrons do not

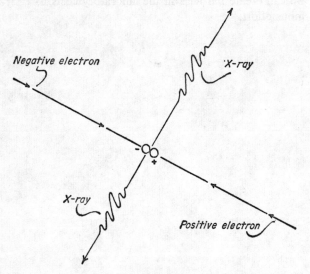

FIG. 4. *Annihilation of positron by electron.*

last very long—they are outnumbered and annihilated by the negative electrons. In this process, the opposite charges of the positive and negative particles neutralize each other.

The creation of particles from energy takes other forms. Always the bombarding particle must have a high enough energy to "pay" for the mass of the particle that is created. As the particles get heavier, the "price" rises accordingly. In the table in Appendix III we see that the energy price for one electron is about 0.5 Mev (a unit to be explained later), and thus to make a pair of them we need about 1 Mev. To create a heavier particle would cost much more in energy. The price of a pion is about 150 Mev, and the price tags for still heavier particles range up to *billions* of electron volts. The ante for the game we are playing with accelerators is very high indeed, and to perfect these machines with which we can create particles in the laboratory costs us enormous effort.

Chapter 2

THE FIRST ACCELERATOR

Before we become acquainted with the most glamorous and complex modern accelerators, we should get on speaking terms with the more approachable and less remote members of the family. The X-ray machine, which we can readily describe as the first accelerator, provides a good introduction. When it was invented, in 1895, it was a wonder of the world, but time and progress have reduced it to humbler status and made it a familiar instrument of everyday living. We shall spend some time on this simple device, the better to appreciate the fundamentals of accelerating particles to high energy, and the easier to see why it has not been possible to get higher and higher energy simply by scaling up existing machines.

As you can see in Fig. 5, the basic X-ray apparatus is nothing more than a glass bulb from which the air has been evacuated and into which two metal pieces, called *electrodes,* have been inserted. The particles it accelerates are electrons, tiny carriers of charge which are part of every atom and are responsible for the flow of electric current through a metallic wire. In the X-ray tube the electrons, instead of being imprisoned in a wire, move in the vacuum.

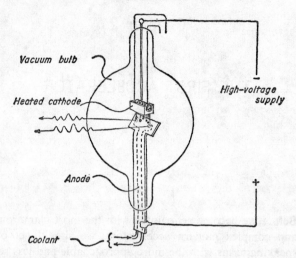

FIG. 5. *X-ray apparatus. The metal cathode, as the diagram shows, is connected to the negative pole of the source of voltage, and the anode is connected to the positive pole. When the cathode is heated, electrons escape from it and, accelerated by the voltage, travel to the anode. On striking the anode, they produce X-rays.*

First, of course, we must have some electrons to set free in the vacuum; a source of particles is the basic requirement of any accelerator. For electrons the source is very easy to arrange. All we have to do is heat up a metal. The electrons in the metal always are moving about, and the heat energy makes them move faster. If the metal is heated enough, some of the electrons will move fast enough to escape from the surface of the metal into the vacuum. Thomas A. Edison observed this phenomenon, called thermionic emission, in 1883 when he was working on his light bulb, and a British engineer, Sir James A. Fleming, was the first to put it to practical use. Radio, television, radar, electronic computers—all electronics using vacuum tubes—depend on thermionic emission of electrons.

Accelerating Electrons

In the X-ray tube of Fig. 5 the wire to be heated, called the *cathode,* is connected to the negative pole of a source of high voltage and is the source supplying electrons. Once the electrons have escaped from the cathode, they can move as they please, since the tube has been evacuated. As you undoubtedly know, like electrical charges repel each other, and unlike charges attract each other. Since the cathode is connected to the negative pole of the voltage source and since the electrons are negatively charged, the cathode repels them.

The metal plate or electrode, called the *anode,* is connected to the positive pole of the high-voltage source and therefore attracts the negative electrons. After they are liberated from the cathode, the electrons move through the vacuum to the anode, gaining speed. They are *accelerated.* When they reach the anode in an ordinary X-ray tube, they are moving at about half the speed of light, a velocity that can be calculated from the force of attraction they experience as they journey from the cathode to the anode. It is plain that the greater the voltage we apply between anode and cathode, the greater will be the attraction and the faster the electrons will move.

If we want to explain this relationship more precisely, we must make a small excursion into mathematics; bear with us briefly, then, for this theoretical interlude, which you can skip over at no loss at all if you find it distasteful.

The kinetic energy of the particle, we learn in the elementary study of electricity, is just equal to the voltage between the electrodes times the electric charge on the particle. (This relationship is, in fact, a good way of *defining* what we mean by voltage.) The kinetic energy, E, is also given by the equation

$$E = \frac{1}{2} mv^2,$$

where m is the mass and v the speed of the particle. Thus we could also write

$$eV = \frac{1}{2} mv^2,$$

where e is the charge and V the voltage. The point of all this is that if we know the voltage difference between the electrodes and the mass and charge of the particle, then we can use this equation to compute the speed. For example, if our X-ray tube has 10 kilovolts across it, then the electrons will have a speed of 6×10^9 cm/sec. Inevitably, the speeds turn out to be so high as to be beyond what we can imagine. Instead of calculating these somewhat meaningless numbers, therefore, physicists have been accustomed to the much simpler device of just referring to the energy of the particles directly, and not their speed. The unit of energy used is the *electron volt,* abbreviated ev; it is the energy acquired by a particle of the same charge as one electron in being accelerated by a voltage of one volt. (Other abbreviations in common use are kev, Mev, and Bev, standing for kilo electron volts, million electron volts, and billion electron volts [Appendix II]. In Europe, billion means a million million, so they speak of Gev, that is, giga electron volts, to correspond to our Bev.) If we accelerate an electron, or a particle of similar charge, by V volts, its energy will then be V electron volts. (We can get the same energy in *joules* by multiplying the number of electron volts by 1.6×10^{-19}.) *One electron volt is the energy each electron acquires in a hypothetical X-ray tube working from a one-volt battery.*

In practice, of course, the voltages used in X-ray machines are much higher than our one volt. The small

X-ray tube used by doctors and dentists might operate with a voltage of 70,000 volts (or 70 kilovolts, abbreviated 70 kv). The electrons in such a tube will have an energy of 70 kev, seventy kilo electron volts.

Roentgen's Radiation

So far we have fitted a glass bulb with two electrodes, evacuated it, and caused electrons to be accelerated between the electrodes. What then? Our reward comes when the electrons striking the anode are brought to an abrupt stop. The electrons, giving up energy just as a bullet gives up energy when it plows into a log, generate electromagnetic waves. Konrad Roentgen discovered this phenomenon in 1895, when he was accelerating electrons in a high-voltage gas-discharge tube.

Roentgen had covered his "cathode tube" with black cardboard and was working in a darkened room. He could see no light coming from his tube, but suddenly, on a table some distance away, a weak light shimmered. When he investigated, he found the mysterious light was coming from a small screen of barium platinocyanide lying on the table. He concluded that some kind of radiation from his tube was exciting the fluorescence. Further experiment showed that the radiation came from spots on the tube wall where the accelerated electrons were striking. It was not the accelerated electrons that caused the barium platinocyanide to fluoresce but another radiation generated when the electrons hit the glass tube.

Roentgen's radiation had the power to penetrate opaque material and to blacken photographic plates. He could take pictures of the bones of his hand with his rays and photograph objects shut up in boxes. For want of a better name he called the mysterious radiation X-rays. Today we know that Roentgen's X-rays are electromagnetic waves very like ordinary light but of much shorter wavelength. Their importance to medical diagnosis and industry comes, of course, from their ability to penetrate bodies that are opaque to visible light.

The Energy of X-Rays

Experimenters after Roentgen investigated many properties of X-rays and found the rays in situations we would associate with wavelike disturbances and with particlelike behavior, too. We have touched on this odd duality already and now must go into it a bit further if we are to have any appreciation at all of the turn physics has taken since the great work of Max Planck and Albert Einstein a half century ago.

In any electromagnetic-wave phenomenon of a given wavelength there is a smallest unit of energy that cannot be further divided. This smallest, discrete package of energy is called a *quantum*. In many ways it behaves as if it were a particle, provided, that is, you are looking for particle behavior. There is a definite energy associated with each quantum of radiation. The shorter the wavelength of the radiation, the higher is the energy of the quantum. An X-ray quantum, for example, has a much higher energy than a quantum of visible light. According to the color, the quantum energy for visible light lies in the range 1.5–2.5 ev. The quantum energy of X-rays, on the other hand, may start around 1 kev (1000 electron volts) and, as the wavelength decreases, go up indefinitely. We call the low-energy X-rays *soft;* easily absorbed, they do not penetrate thick layers of material. The higher the energy, the *harder*—that is, the more penetrating—the X-rays become. In the inspection of very thick and heavy metal castings, extremely hard X-rays with energies up to about 1 Mev (one million electron volts) are used.

When electrons of a certain energy are stopped, the generated X-rays will have a whole range of energies determined by the rate of deceleration of the electron. The energy of the electron itself will set the maximum limit of the X-ray energy. This makes sense; obviously it would be impossible for an electron to produce an X-ray with energy higher than the electron's. If we need very penetrating X-rays, then, we must give high energies to the electrons in the X-ray tube, or, in the language of technology, we must apply a sufficiently high voltage across the tube. This, of course, shifts our attention to another phase of acceleration: How can high voltages be generated?

High Voltages

The simplest method that comes to mind is to connect several low-voltage batteries in series. Suppose we use simple flashlight cells of about 1.5 volts each. If we connect a lot of them together, we obtain a proportionately higher total voltage (1.5 × number of cells). Portable radios, for example, operate on such an arrangement; sixty cells might be needed, for a total of 1.5 × 60, or 90 volts. This method is simple enough but is going to become cumbersome pretty quickly if we want a really high voltage. The Geiger counter used in searching for uranium or other radioactive mineral deposits might take 900 volts, for instance, so the prospector has to tote around a battery of 600 cells. Plainly, if much higher voltages still are required, this scheme soon becomes impracticable.

There are many other uses for high voltages besides the operation of X-ray tubes and other accelerators. For example, the transmission of electric power over long overland lines is more economical at high voltage. (You have seen "high voltage lines" with their long, massive insulators.) The highest voltage in general use for long-distance transmission is 132,000 volts, or 132 kv. Power stations cannot generate such voltages directly, nor can we use them safely in our houses. There have to be devices in the distribution system to change voltage. Such a device is the *transformer*. The transformer can either increase voltage (step it up) from a generator, say, to a high-voltage transmission line, or reduce voltage (step it down) from a high-voltage line to the 120 volts you use at home.

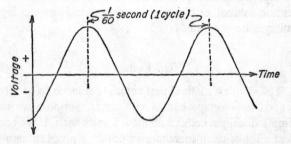

FIG. 6. *Periodic fluctuation of current (A.C.) is plotted in this graph. The observed voltage between two leads of an A.C. outlet is plotted vertically, and time is plotted along the horizontal axis. Note that the curve is smooth and that it reaches voltage peaks on either side of the horizontal axis at intervals of one sixtieth of a second. The voltage plotted above the horizontal axis is of opposite polarity from the voltage below the axis. Where the curve crosses the axis the voltage is momentarily zero as it changes direction.*

An important restriction limits the use of the transformer—it works only for *alternating* current (A.C.). Alternating current now is used almost universally for electrical services, partly because changes of voltage are easy to obtain with transformers. The usual current has a frequency of 60 cycles per second; this means that it goes through sixty complete changes of direction every second. The graph of Fig. 6 shows the periodic fluctuation. Along the vertical axis is plotted the observed voltage between two leads of an A.C. outlet. Time, progressing to the right, is plotted along the horizontal axis. The curve shows each momentary value of the voltage. You can see that the voltage changes smoothly, reaching first a peak in the positive direction, then decreasing through zero and starting toward a peak in the negative direction, that is, voltage of the opposite polarity.

Figure 7 shows what happens when such an alternat-

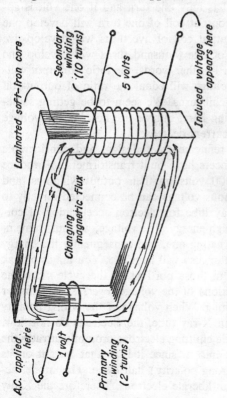

FIG. 7. The relationship between input and output windings is seen in this schematic diagram of a transformer. The fluctuating magnetization of the iron core induces alternating voltage in the output coil. The ten turns of the output winding develop five times the voltage of the two turns of the input winding.

ing voltage is applied to the input winding of a transformer, which consists of an iron core with two coils of wire wound around it. One coil, the input winding, is connected to the source of alternating current, and it magnetizes the iron core as in an electromagnet. The magnetization of the core fluctuates in the same rhythm as the voltage on the input winding. In accordance with a fundamental law of electromagnetism, this fluctuating magnetization will *induce* voltages in any coils wound around the core, and these voltages, in turn, will be alternating in the same rhythm as the input voltage. If the input coil has only one turn and if one volt is applied to it, an output coil of one turn will develop one volt, but an output coil of five turns will develop five volts and one of one thousand turns will develop one thousand volts. In other words, the ratio of output voltage to input voltage will equal the ratio of output-coil turns to input-coil turns. We seem to be getting something for nothing here, but we are not. As the voltage increases, the current decreases.

With great refinements of design, and considerable difficulty, engineers have built transformers to produce up to 2,000,000 volts on their output windings, and such an enormous voltage can be connected directly to a suitable X-ray tube for electron acceleration of correspondingly high energy. The voltage, we must remember, is an alternating one, and consequently the energy of the accelerator also will fluctuate. You may well ask what happens in those portions of the cycle when the polarity (direction) of the voltage *reverses*. The answer is simple: nothing. When voltage of the wrong polarity is applied to an X-ray tube, the electrons do not flow. The hot cathode emitting electrons promptly attracts the electrons back into it, since it is at that instant on its positive (or wrong polarity) half cycle. The anode, being cold, cannot liberate electrons. Therefore the X-ray tube allows electrons to flow only during alternate half cycles of the voltage from the transformer, and the electron energy during those half cycles varies as the instantaneous value of the voltage varies (Fig. 8).

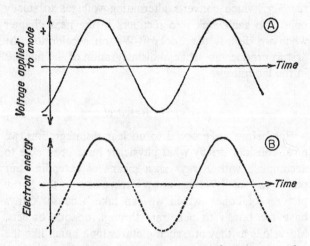

FIG. 8. *Electron energy in an X-ray tube is compared in this graph with the fluctuating voltage and is shown to vary with the instantaneous value of the latter. The dotted portions of the electron curve occur when reversal of the polarity interrupts electron flow.*

If this fluctuation of energy is of no particular consequence, we may get satisfactory performance for many purposes with an X-ray tube operated from alternating current—from "raw" A.C., we would say. Indeed, many X-ray tubes are so run, especially those used in industrial applications and for diagnosis (not treatment) in medicine. But in high-energy physics research, energy fluctuations become very troublesome. A physicist has to know exactly what is going on and be able to control the conditions of his experiment if it is to have meaningful results. Continuous variation of energy would introduce complications that could obscure everything. Hence, almost all particle accelerators employed in research use steady voltage. Some device to treat the raw A.C. and tame it is called for, and we have it in the *rectifier,* which converts alternating voltages to steady ones. We shall look into rectifiers in the next chapter when we discuss the Cockroft-Walton accelerator, the first to produce an artificial disintegration of the nucleus in the laboratory.

X-Rays in Research

But before we proceed to nuclear disintegration, we must consider briefly what physicists have been able to accomplish with X-rays as a means of extending our power to "see." We are not referring now to the X-ray pictures of bones, which we can take because X-rays have the power to penetrate through opaque objects. Marvelous as they are, such pictures look much like the ordinary pictures from a Brownie camera, and taking them is a pretty straightforward matter. The physicist's interest in X-rays concerns a process of "seeing" more complicated than the taking of photographs. As we described in the first chapter, he lets X-rays (or other radiation) strike a substance, and then he tries to figure out in detail how the individual atoms of that substance have reflected, or scattered, the X-rays. We already have outlined how the wavelength of the radiation will limit the amount of detail we can observe. The wavelength of X-rays of typical energy, say 15 kev, is about 10^{-9} cm. It is short enough to be useful within the range of typical atomic distances, about 10^{-8} cm. This makes plain the fundamental advantage of X-rays over visible light. With them, we can probe into the details of atomic structure. Visible light is far too coarse.

Modern crystallography* stands as a monument to research with X-rays. The investigation of diffraction phenomena of X-rays in crystals began in 1912, and the names of Max von Laue and Sir W. Lawrence Bragg are most prominently associated with it. Bragg's studies of the reflection of X-rays from crystals produced startling and beautiful pictures like the one in Plate I. He used the pictures in making detailed analysis of the arrangements of atoms within crystals, with accurate measurements of the interatomic distances. Carried forward over the years, this same line of investigation has yielded extraordinarily detailed knowledge of the orderly arrays of atoms in crystals and led to great accomplishments in fields as seemingly diverse as metallurgy, synthetics, and bacteriology.

We have spoken of the pattern in Plate I as a picture. It is not, of course, a "picture" of anything at all. Think of it instead as a very complicated code transmitted through the X-rays as they are reflected from the atoms in the crystal. It is the scientist's job to break the code. Somehow he must extract the information that it contains in some form, somewhere. Often the scientist finds the secret almost by accident—discoveries are made in many ways. And sometimes many years elapse before someone with just the right insight comes along.

* See *Crystals and Crystal Growing*, by Alan Holden and Phylis Singer (Science Study Series).

Chapter 3

THE EARLY MACHINES: DIRECT ACCELERATORS

The year is 1928 and we stand at the threshold of nuclear physics. For the first time scientists are about to produce artificial disintegration of the nucleus. The consequences of success can be nothing short of revolutionary.

If this introduction sounds dramatic, it is only because it heralds a dramatic story. Even in 1928 the physicists had a keenly developed sense of the achievements in store for them. Since Roentgen first noticed the mysterious shimmer on his platinocyanide screen, that November day in 1895, discoveries in physics had followed one upon another, hot and fast. In 1896, the year after Roentgen's discovery, the French physicist Henri Becquerel discovered the radioactivity of uranium. It was purely by accident, but he took immediate and intelligent advantage of his good luck. The investigators who followed up his findings learned that some of the heaviest atoms, like uranium, undergo spontaneous disintegration; the heavy atoms emit various kinds of radiation and change into lighter ones, the element thereby transmuting into another element. There were signs of strife, then, from within the mysterious atoms!

These radioactive substances, the experiments showed,

emit three kinds of radiation, which were called α-, β-, and γ-rays (*alpha, beta,* and *gamma,* the first three letters of the Greek alphabet). The names were supposed to be temporary until better identification could be obtained, but they have stuck to the present day even though all the rays have been found to be familiar phenomena known in other forms and under other names. Alpha rays are the doubly charged helium atoms thrown out of the disintegrating radioactive substance. Beta rays are nothing but electrons. Gamma rays are very high-energy X-rays. (Remember that the existence of X-rays had been known for only a year and that they are far less energetic than γ-rays.)

Rutherford's Examination of the Atom

The nature of the atom was not then known. J. J. Thomson believed that it might look like a plum pudding—negatively charged particles being interpersed throughout a "sphere of positive electrification." Others thought that all the positive charge might be at the center surrounded by negative charge, or possibly vice versa.

The way to answer this question was to shine a suitable kind of "light" on the atom and study the reflection and scattering. High-energy electrons, accelerated in tubes very like the X-ray tube, were used in the first experiments; but this "light" revealed insufficient detail. Then came the classic work of Lord Rutherford, one of the great experimenters of all time. What he learned in his vastly ingenious, but fundamentally simple, experiments gave us our first really precise insight into the structure and size of the nucleus.

Rutherford turned to the enemy, you might say, for his ammunition. He bombarded atoms with the α-rays supplied in the radioactive disintegration of other atoms. These α-rays are massive and energetic, and their wavelength is short enough to make it possible to "see" much more detail. Rutherford's results were startling. The atom was almost empty!

By far the greatest fraction of the mass of the atom —all but one part in several thousand—Rutherford found to be concentrated in its *nucleus,* yet this nucleus occupied only the tiniest fraction of the volume. If a typical dimension for the entire atom is about 10^{-8} cm (1/100,000,000 cm), the size of the nucleus must be in the order of 10^{-13} cm (1/10,000,000,000,000 cm), or *one hundred thousand times* smaller. Thus Rutherford was the first to see the now familiar picture of the atom: a tiny, massive positively charged core—the nucleus— with a wispy and diffuse cloud of electrons surrounding it.

In 1919 Rutherford, still using nature's ammunition, managed to produce an artificial disintegration of a nucleus. He bombarded nitrogen with α-particles and occasionally observed a disintegration in which the particle must have penetrated into the nitrogen nucleus. The nitrogen nucleus was transformed into a nucleus of oxygen; and a hydrogen nucleus—a proton, that is—was emitted at the same time.

To describe Rutherford's experiment in the laboratory shorthand fashionable today, we write

$$N^{14} + He^4 \rightarrow O^{17} + H^1.$$

In words this means that a nitrogen nucleus of mass 14 units, when struck by a helium nucleus of mass 4 (the α-particle), can change into an oxygen nucleus of mass 17 and a hydrogen nucleus of mass 1 (the proton). Rutherford observed this kind of nuclear reaction with an ingenious apparatus consisting of a brass box that could be evacuated and was fitted with a scintillation screen. A later and more familiar device is the *cloud chamber*. In the latter, conceived in 1896 at the Cavendish Laboratory, Cambridge, England, and perfected by

C. T. R. Wilson, you can watch the tracks of nuclear radiations much as you see the vapor trails of a jet plane across the sky. Plate II is a photograph of such trails in a cloud chamber when a disintegration is occurring.

Alpha particles could disintegrate several other kinds of nuclei, but, as nature supplied them, they were by no means ideal ammunition. In the first place, nature —that is, the disintegration of naturally radioactive sources—is miserly in its production of the particles; they were available only in limited numbers. Secondly, the α-particle carries a double positive charge and so encounters strong repulsion in the target nucleus, which is positive too. And, finally, the large mass of the particle turns out to be a handicap in such work. The experimenters, as the physicists E. U. Condon and George Gamow showed, could look for much better results in the bombardment of nuclei if they could use lighter bullets—protons, for example.

Since nature does not oblige us with fast protons, the investigators faced the problem of accelerating their own. In 1928 the race was on. Who would be the first to achieve an altogether man-arranged disintegration? In England, Cockroft and Walton were at work on their accelerator. At the University of California at Berkeley, Lawrence was working on his cyclotron. At the California Institute of Technology, C. C. Lauritsen was trying to build a transformer device. High in the Alps the Urban group was tempting fate with the scheme to harness lightning bolts. The Englishmen won—but by a narrow margin.

The Cockroft-Walton Machine

The winning Cockroft-Walton accelerator resembled in many ways the X-ray tube we have studied. The main difference, of course, lay in the idea of accelerating protons instead of electrons. For precision, the accelerator operated from a steady voltage and not raw A.C.

Now, where to get protons? As we have seen, a heated cathode, which is just a metallic wire connected to the negative pole of a voltage source, gives us a source of electrons quite readily. But protons are another story. They are in the nucleus of every atom, but they are tightly bound, and we have to pry them loose. Hydrogen with its nucleus of a single proton and with only one electron is the simplest atom. Like all other atoms in their ordinary state, it is electrically neutral. The positively charged nucleus neutralizes the negative charge of the electron. Since it is electrically neutral, we cannot accelerate the atom with an electric voltage. But if we can get rid of the electron and thereby leave the positive nucleus bare, then we have our ammunition ready and armed.

The process of driving off electrons from atoms is called *ionization*. It goes on in all electric discharges through gases—in the luminous neon advertising sign, for example, and in the fluorescent lamp for lighting. In the discharge, electrons collide with neutral atoms of the gas and sometimes knock off atomic electrons. The *ion*, an atom with some of or all its electrons stripped away, is left behind. The hydrogen ion, of course, is the proton. We have met another ion traveling incognito, the stripped helium atom, alias the α-particle.

So, for our source of protons we can use an electric discharge running in hydrogen gas. If we have a small probe with a hole in it and insert this probe into such a discharge, we can draw off some of the ions. Clever inventors have devised all sorts of arrangements for doing this, but the principle remains the same. Such devices are called *ion sources*. With an ion source to provide hydrogen ions, or protons, we are ready for the Cockroft-Walton machine.

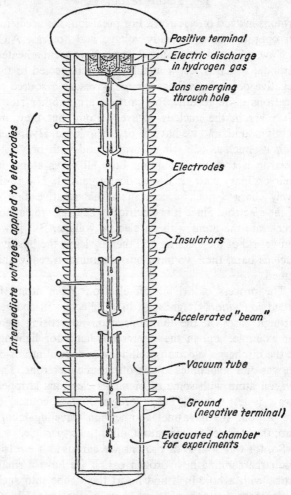

Positive terminal

Electric discharge in hydrogen gas

Ions emerging through hole

Electrodes

Insulators

Accelerated "beam"

Vacuum tube

Ground (negative terminal)

Evacuated chamber for experiments

Intermediate voltages applied to electrodes

FIG. 9. *The Cockroft-Walton accelerating tube is shown in cross section in this diagram. The intermediate electrodes accelerate the ion beam on its journey down the tube. Since the hydrogen ions (protons) are positively charged, they are attracted to the negative terminal at the bottom of the tube.*

Figure 9 shows a cross section of the Cockroft-Walton tube. At the top is the ion source. Because the ions are positive (not negative like the electrons of the X-ray tube), this top end must be made electrically positive. At the bottom of the tube is the negative terminal, which attracts the positive ions, and between the terminals are intermediate electrodes. The chief function of these electrodes is to divide the high voltage into smaller subvoltages and lessen the chance of sparking, or flashover, which would upset the whole operation. The electrodes have the additional function of directing the ions into a fairly well-defined path, or trajectory; by the time the ions have been accelerated along the tube, they are traveling in quite a narrow bundle, or *beam*. The narrowness of the beam is important. We want the ions to emerge through a hole in the negative terminal and so to give us, in a manageable bundle, the high-energy protons we need for experiments in nuclear physics.

The accelerating tube must be carefully evacuated, usually to several billionths of an atmosphere, and so must the confined space outside the tube where the experiments are to be performed with the emerging beam. This gives us our accelerator complete and ready for action except for the necessary high voltage.

Since we want a steady voltage and not an alternating one, we cannot use a transformer directly. We shall need the *rectifier* we mentioned earlier. You might think of a rectifier as a one-way electrical valve. With such a valve, we can suppress the sections of alternating voltage which have the wrong polarity. But this still leaves us with a pulsating voltage when we want a steady one. This is not too much of a problem. If we add a reservoir of electric charge (a *capacitor,* or *condenser*), we can hoard enough charge between the cycle peaks to tide us

over. Figure 10 illustrates the process. With a large
enough reservoir, we have an almost steady voltage at
the output.

You have met the rectifier already but probably did
not recognize it. An X-ray tube acts as one. Remember
that only the X-ray tube's heated cathode liberates electrons, not the cold anode. The current therefore can flow
in only one direction, with the electrons leaving the cathode. Vacuum rectifier tubes on this principle have been

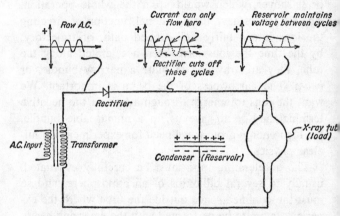

FIG. 10. *Steady voltage is obtained with apparatus
including a rectifier and a condenser. A.C. voltage from
the transformer produces the familiar curve (Fig. 6) in
the upper-left graph. The rectifier, a one-way electric
valve, suppresses the voltage of one polarity (the curve
below the horizontal axis) and allows current flow in
only one direction, as in the upper-middle graph. The
voltage no longer is alternating, but it still pulsates.
Storing electric charge in the condenser maintains the
voltage between cyclic peaks and gives an almost steady
voltage at the output.*

designed to perform the function efficiently without either wasting voltage or generating many X-rays. There are all sorts of special applications for rectifiers of this kind, but they can handle only limited voltage. If they are forced beyond their limit, breakdown—the sparking phenomenon that is such a nuisance in other high-voltage work—will spoil their operation.

To bypass this limitation, Cockroft and Walton did more than rectify the alternating voltage from their transformer; they had a whole network of rectifiers and reservoirs connected cleverly to obtain a total output voltage much higher than the voltage from the transformer. This kind of circuit is called a voltage multiplier. You can picture it best if you think of a whole stack of reservoirs, one on top of another, with electric charge being pumped from reservoir to reservoir through one-way valves, and with the pumping action of the transformer providing the motive power. Each stage of the circuit, in fact, bears a considerable resemblance to the ordinary water hand pump.

If there are ten stages in the Cockroft-Walton circuit, there are ten reservoirs stacked up, and each is charged to the voltage of the transformer. Thus the output voltage is much higher than the input. The output from the top one of ten reservoirs is ten times the input voltage. Intermediate levels—nine, eight, seven, etc., times the input voltage—are available down the stack. The intermediate levels serve to divide the high voltage up in a regular manner and thus help to prevent breakdown. It is possible also to connect them to the intermediate electrodes of the accelerating tube.

The first Cockroft-Walton generators stood in the open in a large room, but the arrangement limited the voltage that could be reached without flashover between the high-voltage terminal and the walls of the room. The flashover phenomenon was used, in fact, for a rough measurement of the voltage achieved by the machine. A rather gruesome story goes with this. The early workers on Cockroft-Walton generators used to measure the voltage they had achieved by bringing a grounded metal sphere close to the machine and observing at what distance sparking would take place. The greater the distance, of course, the higher the voltage and the happier the physicists. The physicist would slowly walk up a stepladder placed below the high-voltage terminal, carefully holding the metal sphere on a stick above his head. A long wire trailed from the sphere, its other end attached to a water pipe. As the physicist climbed, he would count the number of steps. When flashover occurred to the sphere, he would know the distance approximately and be able to tell whether the voltage was high or not. The electric discharge, of course, traveled down the wire and into the grounded water pipe. You can guess what happened one day: the wire came undone from the pipe, and the physicist, unaware of this, proudly climbed up his stepladder once more. The flash occurred, but this time it went not through the wire but through the physicist, who was thrown violently to the ground. Laid up for several weeks in the hospital, he was little appeased when told that the voltage had been particularly high that day! (It is also rumored that a pair of charred footsteps could be seen on the stepladder where he had stood.)

These stories make popular folklore for physicists, of course, but it is true that the element of danger is not absent from work with accelerators, and that in a way this adds spice to the dish. We shall come across instances of this danger from time to time; electrocution is only one hazard, radiation being, of course, the chief concern.

In Plate III you can see the most famous of the

Cockroft-Walton machines, built in the 1930s at the Cavendish Laboratory by the Philips Company of Holland. This accelerator works at a little over a million volts, but if you try to run the voltage up higher, a deafening report will tell you that lightning has just struck! In each flashover the spark digs a pockmark, rather like a bullet hole, in the concrete wall.

If you wanted to raise the voltage of the accelerator much higher, you would need better insulation, and the best way to get it would be to envelop the accelerator in a gas at a pressure higher than atmospheric. (You could immerse the whole thing in oil, but anyone who has had to work with large tanks of oil will tell you it is better to steer clear of this alternative.) Unfortunately, it is not easy to enclose the Cockroft-Walton in a high-pressure tank. The machine is bulky and complicated; the tank would have to be very large and the walls very heavy. So, practicality limits the energy range available with a Cockroft-Walton. Nowadays we look on the device as a specialized instrument suitable for relatively low voltages only, say in the range of up to about a million volts. Above this level, other machines have superseded it. The Cockroft-Walton does remain a valuable stand-by, however, and it finds frequent use as a *pre-accelerator* for injecting particles into more advanced machines, which may themselves be incapable of getting the particles "off the ground." Humble service, perhaps, but important nonetheless.

Van de Graaff's Electrostatic Generator

We must consider, then, some alternative sources of high voltage to replace the Cockroft-Walton voltage multiplier. Remember that we can leave the accelerating tube with its accessories untouched, but we do need a different high-voltage supply, preferably one that is simpler and more compact than the stack of reservoirs and rectifiers.

It has been known for a long time that *static electricity* can generate very high voltages. This is the kind of electricity that gives you a spark when you drag your feet on carpet and then touch a doorknob; you can obtain it by rubbing together certain materials. On the grand scale it causes lightning. In fact, it was in the static form that electricity was first discovered by the ancients. The Greeks noticed that some materials electrified by friction would attract small objects and sometimes emit little sparks. Amber was a favorite material for these experiments, and the Greek name for amber is *elektron*. Thus does language often record history.

Examples of static electricity have a curious habit, though, of falling either into the class of the trivial or into that of the gigantic. Thus we can talk of drawing sparks after walking across a rug on a dry day: this makes a nice demonstration, but hardly seems appropriate for a major exercise in engineering. At the other extreme we might consider the phenomenon of lightning, which is also caused by static electricity. Here at once we find ourselves in the realm of the mighty and overpowering! It is thus a major triumph to design an electrostatic machine which falls between these extreme limits.

Robert J. Van de Graaff's generator, invented at Princeton University around 1930, is tame and tractable, yet powerful enough to feed some of the most useful particle accelerators. It is the descendant of a long series of electrostatic generators, such as the Wimshurst machine, which you probably have met before. There must be hundreds of Van de Graaff machines in use today, ranging in size from a couple of feet to a couple of stories. Research, medicine, and industry all need them.

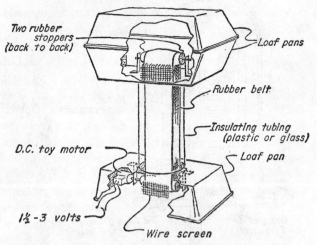

Two rubber stoppers (back to back)

Loaf pans

Rubber belt

Insulating tubing (plastic or glass)

D.C. toy motor

Loaf pan

1½ -3 volts

Wire screen

FIG. 11. *Make-it-yourself Van de Graaff generators of this type have produced voltages as high as 100,000. You can use ordinary dime-store metal baking pans for the base and the dome of the generator. The shaft between the base and the dome can be a glass or plastic cylinder; a plastic fruit-juice mixer is fine. The rubber belt is inside this cylinder, so holes must be cut in the top of the base and the bottom of the generator dome. Each of the pulleys on which the belt runs can be made of two rubber stoppers slipped over a piece of glass tubing as an axle. One of the pulleys, either one, should be covered with aluminum foil. The two pieces of wire screen should be on the side of the belt that moves upward. They must be screwed or bolted to the base and the dome to establish electrical connections. The screens should be not more than an eighth of an inch from the belt. The wire ends of the screens form the fingers along which electric charge flows onto and off the belt. The belt can be made of any low-carbon rubberized insulating material. The toy motor must be firmly screwed or bolted down, of course, if it is to drive the belt.*

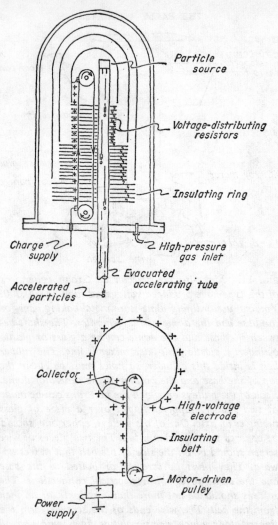

Particle source

Voltage-distributing resistors

Insulating ring

Charge supply

High-pressure gas inlet

Evacuated accelerating tube

Accelerated particles

Collector

High-voltage electrode

Insulating belt

Motor-driven pulley

Power supply

FIG. 12. *Workings of an actual Van de Graaff generator are shown schematically in the simplified diagram at the top. The bottom diagram shows the flow of electric charge when the machine is in operation. Note that it is distributed all over the spherical dome.*

For years one major commercial concern has devoted itself exclusively to manufacture of this accelerator.

Before we explain the Van de Graaff machine in detail, you might try a simple experiment. The first part you can do with no more apparatus than your own hair and a comb; the second part you will have to complete in your imagination. On a dry day, or in an old house with hot-air heat and no humidifying system, run a comb through your hair. Hear it crackle and see how the hairs cling to the comb. What is happening is that the comb is removing free electrons from the hair molecules. The loss of electrons leaves your hair positively charged, and the gain of electrons makes the comb negative. Opposite charges attract; the hair clings.

Suppose, now, you had a sort of continuous comb, like a ribbon. As you pulled the ribbon through your hair, it would remove electrons continuously and carry them away. If at some distant point you had a device to remove the electrons from the ribbon and store them, you would be achieving higher and higher voltage. This is not the exact Van de Graaff principle, but there are similarities. On this method you can make a small generator which on a dry day will build up as much as 30,000 volts. Figure 11 shows how.

In diagram, the actual Van de Graaff machine (Fig. 12) looks quite simple; it gets its efficiency from careful engineering and a trick. Our diagram shows a belt on pulleys running up into a large roughly spherical housing or electrode of highly polished metal. The housing is supported on an insulated column. The belt, which is made of rubberized fabric or some other insulating material and moves at high speed, is our "continuous comb." The polished electrode is our voltage reservoir. The source of charge for the belt commonly is another, smaller generator; the charge from this source is "sprayed" onto the belt from a set of fine points. De-

pending on the polarity desired, we can load up the belt
with either negative charges (electrons) or with positive
charges. The belt is wide, perhaps two feet or so, and it
travels as fast as possible, maybe 60 miles an hour.
Thus, it can transport a lot of charge to the top terminal.

The trick at the heart of the machine is the mounting
of the upper pulley *inside* the spherical housing. Electric
charges on the belt, repelled by all the other charges on
the belt, leave through "pick-off" fingers and move to
the *outside* surface of the housing, which is the high-
voltage electrode, or terminal, of the device. Even when
the outside of the electrode is crowded with electricity,
there is no difficulty getting charge off the belt. This is
because the charges on the outside surface, repelling
each other strongly, force themselves into such a position that a new charge, arriving from the inside, is repelled *equally* from all directions and so meets no net
opposition at all.

The rounding of the housing terminal and the high
polish of the metal are engineering points that contribute
to making the machine work. Electric stress tends to be
greatest at sharp corners and points, and breakdowns
readily start from such points. Sharp corners or surface
irregularities would cause spark breakdown before the
desired high voltage could be built up on the housing.

The Van de Graaff generator is a very compact device and a simple one. For better insulation late designs
are enclosed in chambers filled with inert gas under high
pressure. A typical such accelerator is shown in Plate
IV with the high-pressure tank opened. Here the heart
of the machine, its fast-moving belt, is not visible, unfortunately. It is surrounded on all sides by specially
shaped electrodes which serve to divide up the high-
voltage stress into many sections of smaller stress. The
effort to prevent high-voltage breakdown is thus the
dominating aspect of this machine. With all the strate-

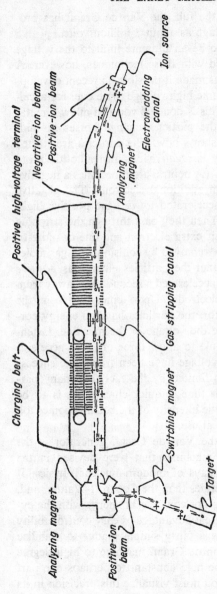

FIG. 13. *The tandem Van de Graaff changes a negative-ion beam into a positive-ion beam to accomplish a double acceleration. Positive ions from the ion source at the right pick up electrons in the electron-adding canal and, passing through the analyzing magnet, form a negative-ion beam of ions of the correct mass and energy. In the main vacuum tube the negative ions are accelerated to the terminal, which is kept at a high positive voltage by the charging-belt system. Passing into a second canal, the beam loses electrons in the presence of a gas and emerges as a positive-ion beam accelerated away from the high positive electrode.*

gems exploited to the full, the Van de Graaff has produced voltages as high as about 7 million volts.

There appears to be an ultimate limit to the voltage
that can be reached with these techniques, however. A
clever strategem has made it possible, in recent developments, to use the same high voltage twice over for accelerating particles. This is done, if you will allow a meta-
phor, by making the particles change horses in mid-
stream! Figure 13 shows how. The particles are started
out on their journey as *negative* ions, instead of the more
usual positive ones. (A neutral atom becomes a negative
ion by capturing an additional electron.) The negative
particles are first accelerated *toward* the positive high-
voltage electrode. Then they pass through the stripping
canal, in which their extra electron and one or more of
the built-in ones are removed by collision with gas molecules. From the canal the particles emerge as *positive*
ions. Now they are accelerated a second time, away from
the high-voltage electrode. Upon emerging from the
"tandem" accelerator, the particles have an energy corresponding to twice the voltage of the machine. Exten-
sions of this principle to allow three or more accelerations by the same voltage have been tried. The success
of such schemes is limited by the fact that many particles are lost each time a quick-change act is to be
staged. Ultimately the intensity of the beam becomes too
low to be of practical use.

In many ways the Van de Graaff generator is the
tame giant of the machines that were devised in the
early and exciting days of modern nuclear physics. It
achieves higher energies than the Cockroft-Walton, and,
even though it does not compete in energy with the cyclotron, it has the great advantage of easy controllability
and precision. It is a fairly simple matter to stabilize
the voltage of a Van de Graaff machine to high degree
—the energy may be held constant to perhaps one part
in ten thousand! You must visualize this precision in its

historical context—a few years earlier, such high-voltage devices could not be made to function at all.

The benefits of this great stability show up when the time comes in a research problem to consolidate initial discoveries and fill in the necessary detail to buttress proposed theories. With these machines investigators amassed a wealth of information describing all kinds of nuclear reactions and disintegrations. At first, this information appeared to be hopelessly complex and confusing, for there are hundreds of species of nuclei, each with a detailed and specific response to bombardment by particles of different energies. A similar situation confronted the first spectroscopists who analyzed the colored light emitted by different kinds of atoms under suitable stimulation. In the end, the atomic spectroscopists were able to build up a remarkably successful theory of atomic structure: and with the magic wand of this theory, the confused spectral structure could be sorted out, classified, and understood in every detail. Progress in *nuclear spectroscopy* has not yet brought us a complete understanding of the structure of the nucleus, but the wealth of experimental detail obtained with such precision accelerators as the Van de Graaff already has given us a great amount of insight. Many regularities were discovered in the listings of the nuclear responses, and these have led to elegant theories of nuclear structure that show some unexpected similarities with atomic structure.

This field of research is by no means exhausted yet, but already it is known as classical nuclear physics. Such is the speed at which we move nowadays. The rapid advances are a testimony to the constructive relationship between research physicists and accelerator builders —they work hand in glove. As a matter of fact, they wear the same gloves. Machine building has always been the research physicist's hobby.

Chapter 4

LINEAR ACCELERATORS

So far we have discussed only accelerators in which we apply a high voltage between two electrodes and accelerate particles directly from one electrode to the other. When the particle emerges, it has an energy, measured in electron volts, that is directly equivalent to the applied voltage. These systems, unfortunately, suffer from a troublemaker, which we have mentioned several times. When we try to increase the voltage above a few million volts, premature discharges, which we call "spurious," occur. At high voltage there can be sparking through the gas surrounding the electrode, or a breakdown may occur in the evacuated tube in which the particles travel. The discharges short out the voltage and ruin the operation.

To overcome this sort of limitation, a more subtle system of acceleration must be found, one in which the particles are not accelerated in one giant step by the action of a very high voltage, but rather in many small, successive steps. Each act of acceleration then does not need to employ a very high voltage. In the 1930s, R. Wideröe, in Germany, devised such a system. He envisaged giving the particles many small pushes in succession, rather than one single big push. If the little

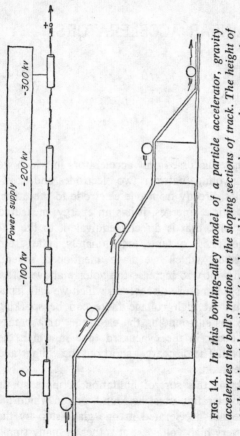

FIG. 14. *In this bowling-alley model of a particle accelerator, gravity accelerates the ball's motion on the sloping sections of track. The height of each horizontal section of track would correspond to a voltage source in a real particle accelerator. The amount of acceleration the ball would undergo is strictly limited by the difference in level between the top and the foot of the entire track.*

pushes can be properly timed, then their effects add up, and the particles will reach a very high energy. To illustrate this system, we use a trick that proves very valuable in scientific thought. We construct a model of the new device we are trying to understand, and we use for our model components that are already well understood and familiar. Then, with ideas obtained with the help of the model, we can return to the actual problem and see how these ideas fit.

A Mechanical Analog

As a model for a particle accelerator we shall use a ball rolling along a grooved track, such as bowling alleys have for returning the balls to the players (Fig. 14). The track slopes downhill, and the action of gravity accelerates the ball. You will easily see how the *height* of the track corresponds to the *voltage* in a particle accelerator.

If we want the ball to move very fast, we need a track that has a large difference in level between the beginning and the end. Ultimately construction difficulties may limit the height we can obtain—they correspond to the breakdown limitations that we encounter with high voltages. How could we accelerate balls even faster than is possible with the highest track? In the hope of obtaining repeated accelerations, we might try dividing up the track into sections, as illustrated in Fig. 15, *A*. But this leads us nowhere. The uphill pieces of track slow the ball down again, and the final speed depends only on the *total* level difference between the start and the finish, not on how the intermediate sections are shaped. Switchback or roller-coaster designers have long been familiar with this fact.

We conclude that with a *fixed* track there is no way of circumventing the limitation imposed by a given dif-

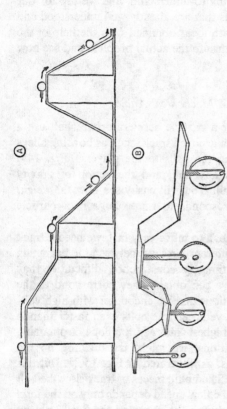

FIG. 15. The fixed-track arrangement, A, although it has some extra-steep descents, makes the ball pay for these by having to climb the intermediate rises. Over-all gain of speed is thus the same as if the track had been laid out smoothly, as in Fig. 14. In the arrangement at B, the horizontal sections move up and down, carrying the ball with them. If the timing is right, the ball can always be moving downhill between sections, never having to climb any hill.

ference in levels. If we are willing to make the track movable, however, then great new possibilities are opened up. Consider the track shown in Fig. 15, *B*. Here there are several sections, each mounted on a crank that moves the section up and down rhythmically. Flexible pieces connect the sections so the ball can roll smoothly from one to the next. Now, suppose we start a ball rolling when the first section is just at a high level, while the second is low. The ball will roll *downhill* into the second section, and so be accelerated. Then, while the ball is rolling along the second section, we have the section move up to a higher level on its crank; meanwhile, the third section moves down, ready to receive the ball. In this way the ball can be allowed to move downhill between each pair of sections, and thus be continually accelerated. Note that the ball is carried up again by the motion of each section as a whole, not by rolling uphill. The section remains level while it moves; the ball is not slowed down at all.

Wideröe's idea is beautifully simple. We can summarize it by saying that the ball is *pumped* up to higher levels by the motion of the sections, rather than having to *coast* up as it did on the fixed track of Fig. 15, *A*.

It might be amusing to build a ball track along these lines, but probably the mechanical difficulties would get the better of you. Imagine, though, the fun you could have at a bowling alley with such a device! The unsuspecting bowler sees the ball coming toward him, with a level difference of maybe a foot or so, and expects it to roll leisurely up to him. Instead, the track gives a few convulsive wriggles, rather like a caterpillar, and the ball comes shooting out at the end with tremendous speed! As a matter of fact, this is exactly the principle that the surf rider uses.

Before we use our model to teach us more details about this sort of acceleration, let us quickly see how an accelerator on this principle would look. We have seen that height of track corresponds to *voltage*. So the movable sections must correspond to electrodes whose voltage varies rhythmically. It is easy to see that this can be achieved if the voltage supply is not a steady one, but instead uses alternating current (A.C.). You will also recall that successive sections of track had to move in opposite directions, to permit the ball always to cross downhill. This requires that successive electrodes in our accelerator be connected to opposite poles of our source of A.C.

Now let us return to the track model and see what design features it must have if it is to work efficiently. The first obvious requirement is that the ball should remain *in step* with the pumping action of the track; otherwise, it will no longer receive an acceleration at each successive section. If all the sections move up and down in the same rhythm (as they would if they were all connected to the same rotating shaft by their cranks), then the ball must spend the *same time* in each section, the time required to go from the bottom to the top. Since the ball is getting faster along the way, we must make successive sections correspondingly longer. This idea has already been tacitly incorporated in the diagram of Fig. 15, *B*.

At this stage, it might seem a little hopeless to make a very good accelerator along these lines. If the design calls for many sections, then it seems difficult to maintain the correct timing with any accuracy. What if the ball gets held up a little in one section, say by a piece of grit? Will the rest of the schedule be completely ruined? And what if the ball is not started on its run at just the right moment? Any design that relies entirely on an absolute schedule, or we might say on *dead reckoning,* is obviously very vulnerable. Fortunately, there is an intrinsic sort of stability in the motion of our ball down the track, which permits it to correct automatically for small errors as they arise. Wideröe foresaw this stability, and it is this elegant feature that makes the design so successful.

Automatic Timing Stability

We must examine in detail how the timing of the ball affects the amount of acceleration it receives. Obviously, the push it gets depends on the level difference between the sections at that moment; and since the sections move up and down rhythmically, we get a diagram like the one in Fig. 16. Here, the push is plotted vertically, while the horizontal axis represents the passage of time. The

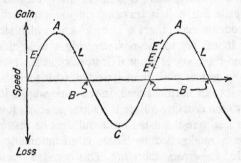

FIG. 16. *This phase diagram shows how the push given to the ball at a crossing between sections of track varies with the timing.*

maximum push comes at the instant *A*, when the sections are in their most favorable relative positions. At later times the push becomes less; finally, at *B*, the sections are momentarily on the same level, and no push results. At still later times the ball would have to move uphill—we get a negative push. From this diagram, then, we can read the acceleration of the ball if we know its time of arrival relative to the motion of the track. This time, relative to a periodic motion, is usually called the *phase;* the diagram of Fig. 16 is also known as a phase diagram.

When we design our track, it would be best not to call for the maximum possible push at each stage; such a greedy design leaves no margin for error. Instead, suppose we are content with a somewhat smaller acceleration. Our timetable might then have the ball cross at a time such as *E* on the phase diagram, or the same result could be obtained at point *L*. Schedule *E* might be called the early route, and *L* the late route. As far as acceleration is concerned, the two schedules are equivalent; but in a moment we will see that *E* has a very desirable stability, while *L* is not similarly blessed.

Suppose our ball is traveling on the early schedule and suddenly encounters a piece of grit, which slows it down. It will get to the next crossing a little after the expected time, say at point *E'* instead of at *E*. It will get a slightly greater push than expected, which will help to restore it to its normal speed. In the same way, if it were to get to the crossing a little too soon, as at *E"*, it would receive less than the usual push and thus be restored to a more normal schedule. There is an automatic compensation for errors, therefore. This is called *phase stability,* and its importance in the design of almost all modern accelerators cannot be overstated. We shall have occasion to emphasize this point again and again.

(You may want to think out for yourself why there is no phase stability in the "late" schedule, at *L* in Fig. 16. This little exercise will give you a better understanding of what we have been saying—it's a basic idea, and the effort is well worth while.)

The magic of phase stability has a very far-reaching effect on our accelerators. Think back for a moment to the ball track we planned to install at the bowling alley,

to astonish the unsuspecting bowlers. We have the track
all made and wriggling gently, but suppose we feed the
ball in carelessly, even at random. If we happen to hit
a good time, the ball will be caught up in the undulations
of the track and be accelerated as planned. It will be
drawn by phase stability into the early schedule *E,* even
if it started out with some error. On the other hand, if
the starting error was too great and phase stability
failed to correct the motion of the ball, there will be no
acceleration at all. (The ball might even be shot back
out from the track toward us.) So, within certain limits,
the track is a tolerant sort of device, accepting balls even
with a certain error of timing. All the balls that are
accepted are drawn toward the same phase. It would
remain to examine just how the balls finally *reach* that
phase, but this would take us too far afield. It turns out
that they generally overshoot the right timing, then get
drawn back again, overshoot once more, and so on. In
other words, they *oscillate* about the correct phase. In
most accelerators (although not in all) these oscillations
are fairly quickly damped out, so that at the end of the
acceleration period, the balls (we mean particles, of
course) are moving very close to the design schedule.
They are bunched together in time and emerge in little
bursts. This effect is called *phase bunching.*

By now, our track model has taught us a great deal
about this type of acceleration. The actual particle accelerators using this principle are called *linear accelerators,* which is perhaps not a very good name. (After all,
the direct accelerators we have seen in the last chapter
are also linear, that is, they operate along a straight
path.) But the name is generally accepted; colloquially
it is often abbreviated to *linac.*

Linac Design

The connection between our model and the actual machine is so close that we need not spend very long over describing the linac in detail. A diagrammatic view is shown in Fig. 17. At the left we have the usual ion source. Then comes a succession of hollow electrodes, each longer than its predecessor; these correspond to the movable sections of track. The particles are accelerated as they cross the gap from one electrode to the next; within each electrode they are shielded from voltage differences and therefore move at constant speed.

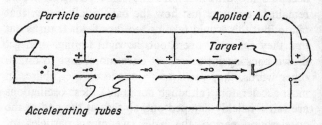

FIG. 17. *The arrangement of accelerating electrodes in a linac is shown schematically in this diagram, in which the particle path extends from the source at the left to the target at the right. Notice that each electrode is longer than the one before it, and that when one electrode is positive, the two on either side are negative.*

Technically, this constant motion is called *drift* (again a rather misleading word, for the particles "drift" with great purpose and usually at enormous speeds!). The hollow electrodes are also called drift tubes. They are connected to a source of alternating voltage in such a way that while one electrode is positive, both its neighbors are negative, and vice versa.

In the design of a linac the path length obviously is

important. When a proton acquires an energy of 10 Mev, it is traveling about 4×10^9 cm per second. This is impressively fast. (For comparison, the speed of an auto going 60 miles an hour is about 3×10^3 cm/sec, and the speed of light is 3×10^{10} cm/sec.) If we take 100 cm, which is a little more than 3 feet, as a convenient length for the longest and final electrode of our linac, the others will turn out to be conveniently short. We can find the time it takes the particle to traverse the electrode by dividing its length, 10^2 cm, by the speed, 4×10^9 cm/sec, and get 2.5×10^{-8} seconds.

If the particle is to remain in step with the applied voltage, the time must correspond to a half cycle of the voltage, and the time for a full cycle is therefore 5×10^{-8} seconds. The frequency is equal to one divided by the time for a full cycle, which gives 2×10^7. (Refer to Appendix II if you have trouble with this kind of calculation and would like to learn more about it and about units in general.)

Now, 2×10^7, or twenty megacycles per second (20 Mc/s), is a very high frequency. It is in the realm of frequencies used for radio communication. The ordinary broadcast band, for example, covers the range of frequencies from 0.55 to 1.6 Mc/s, and adjoining at higher frequencies are the bands for police, Coast Guard, and international short-wave broadcasters. It is a frequency with which we have had lots of technical experience, and this familiarity contributes to making the linac a good system for giving particles more energy than can be obtained with direct high-voltage sources.

But the linac does suffer from the practical disadvantage that very many electrodes must be used for a high final energy. For example, consider our 10-Mev proton and assume that the maximum voltage we could apply to any one electrode would be 0.5 Mv. (With a frequency as high as 20 Mc/s even this voltage would be quite a trick!) If the protons received the maximum possible acceleration at each gap at this voltage, it would take 20 sections to build up the full 10 Mev; if we wanted to go to 100 Mev, it would take 200 sections. We must remember, too, that the sections have to be of different lengths. If the final one is not to be impossibly long, the first probably will have to be very short, and this may be hard to arrange. So, while our linac does offer the possibility of very high energies, achieving them turns out to be hard work.

For a compromise, it is customary to start the particles out on their linac journey at high velocity—that is, to "inject" them from a smaller pre-accelerator like the Van de Graaff or Cockroft-Walton. Then the first electrodes need not be impossibly short. A direct accelerator giving the particles an energy of 100 to 200 kev might be a good injector.

In a linac for protons, successive drift tubes are mounted in a big evacuated chamber. Currents of a suitable distribution are set up in a liner inside this chamber, and the electrodes are fed with radio-frequency voltages of the correct polarity. The arrangement permits the voltage to build up to a high value at the particular frequency of operation—it is a *tuned* system, also called a *resonator*. To generate the needed high voltages at radio frequencies still takes very large amounts of power, and it is impractical to attempt to sustain this level of operation continuously. Besides, many of the components, such as the radio tubes used to generate the voltage, cannot operate continuously at these high power levels. They would overheat and break down. So we get around these limitations by making only a brief stab at operation from time to time, and letting components recover in the intervening rest periods. This mode of operation is called *pulsed* operation and is common for very high-energy accelerators. Figure 18

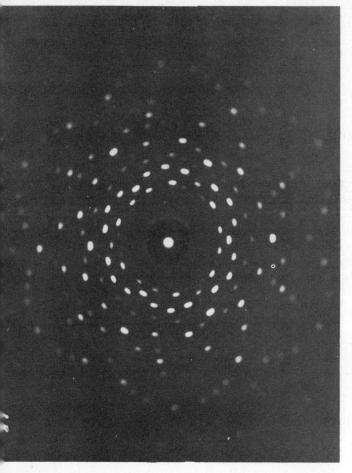

PLATE I. In this X-ray photograph of a quartz crystal the striking quality is symmetry. The crystal's atomic planes deflected the X-rays as they traveled along one of the crystal's axes of symmetry. Professor B. E. Warren, of M.I.T., took the photograph; the German physicist Max von Laue originated the method.

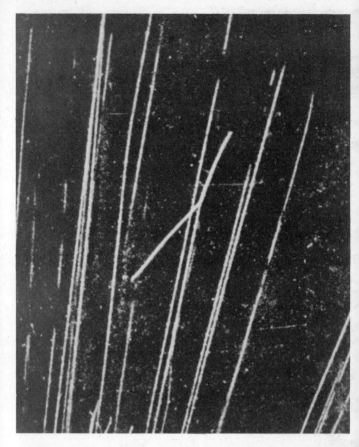

PLATE II. In this cloud-chamber photograph, taken by the British physicist P. M. S. Blackett, you can see the tracks of several alpha particles. In the center a particle has collided with a nitrogen nucleus and produced an "alpha fork." One branch of the fork is the track of an oxygen isotope nucleus, the other of a hydrogen nucleus, or proton.

PLATE III. The 1.4-Mev Cockroft-Walton accelerator at Cavendish Laboratory, Cambridge, England. The white tube with rings at the left is the accelerating tube. At its top is the ion source in the high-voltage terminal. The black column to the right houses belt driving generator in terminal. The assemblage at the right consists of two condenser stacks with rectifier tubes. Experiments with accelerated ions are conducted in room below.

PLATE IV. Large (5-Mev) Van de Graaff generator is shown here with its pressure cover (upper right) removed. Note the polish of the high-voltage terminal at top. Rings around the column are voltage dividers. In this M.I.T. installation the laboratory for experiments with beams is below the machine.

PLATE V. The size of the Stanford University linac is suggested in this view of a small section of the machine. Accelerating tube s at the left. The crosswise tubes installed at intervals along the line are waveguides to conduct radio-frequency power to the tube.

PLATE VI. Evolution of the cyclotron: At top, the first useful cyclotron, designed by the late Ernest O. Lawrence and M. Stanley Livingston (now at M.I.T.), developed 1.2 Mev and had polefaces 11 inches in diameter. The cover has been removed and a dee is visible at right. Bottom picture shows the vacuum chamber and one dee of the 27-inch cyclotron, the second stage of cyclotron development, also designed by Lawrence and Livingston with the University of California group.

PLATE VII. The magnets were the most conspicuous components of the 11-inch cyclotron, as they are in modern machines. Vacuum chamber, with the dees, is between the two magnet poles.

PLATE VIII. M. Stanley Livingston (left) and Ernest O. Lawrence are shown here with

shows the pulses of operation, with rest periods between them, in the over-all output of a typical linac. During each pulse, of course, the protons arrive in little bursts due to phase bunching. The duration of each pulse might be 10 or 100 microseconds (one microsecond = $1\mu\text{sec}$ = one millionth of a second); there might be sixty such pulses every second.

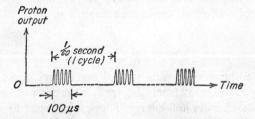

FIG. 18. *Pulsed operation in the output of a linac is shown in this graph with the machine's output plotted against time. The pulses, with rest periods between, are shown lasting 100 microseconds and occurring 60 times a second. At each pulse protons arrive in bursts, due to the bunching by the accelerating voltage.*

The linear-accelerator technique has also been applied with particular success to the production of very high-energy *electrons*. As you know, electrons are much lighter particles than protons—about 2000 times lighter. If you give a certain amount of energy to an electron, it will travel much faster than would a proton of the same energy. This is no different from everyday experience. A small bullet shot from a rifle may carry a certain energy, but with the same energy you could accelerate a big truck only to a very much lower speed. Imagine how much energy there would be in a truck moving as fast as a bullet! Previously, we calculated that the speed of a 10-Mev proton was 4×10^9 cm/sec. What would be the speed of a 10-Mev *electron*? If we calculated this in an innocent way, we would get an answer that would be much higher than the speed of light. Before the advent of the Theory of Relativity in 1905, such an answer would have been accepted without a grumble. Nobody then imagined that there could be an absolute speed limit. But Einstein's theory proposed that nothing could move faster than light—3×10^{10} cm/sec, or about 186,-000 miles per second. We are very familiar with this idea of a universal speed limit nowadays.

Crowding the Speed Limit

Another fundamental idea of the Theory of Relativity, you will recall from Chapter 1, is the complete equivalence of mass and energy. Suppose we start to speed up an electron. In giving it energy, we also increase its mass, and it becomes progressively harder to accelerate. Ultimately, the electron's mass becomes so great that we can increase its speed only by infinitesimal amounts. This is the explanation of the universal speed limit. When particles approach this limit, their energy is so high, and they therefore have become so heavy, that they can hardly be accelerated further.

Because electrons are so much lighter, they start to approach the speed limit at lower energies than do protons or other heavy particles. The mass of an electron has an energy equivalent of about 0.5 Mev; every electron carries this amount of energy around with it, disguised as mass. If we accelerate an electron to 0.5 Mev, its *total* energy will really be 1 Mev—we must add the mass-energy to the energy in the motion (kinetic energy). Already we have doubled the total energy of the electron, or—to use the other name for it—we have doubled the mass of the electron. Electrons of 0.5-Mev kinetic energy are twice as heavy as electrons at rest! So they do not have to move faster than our speed limit; they just become heavier. In Fig. 19, we have plotted the speed of electrons at various energies. We can see that at 2 Mev they already have reached within 2 per cent of the velocity of light, and at 10 Mev they crowd the limit to within about 0.1 per cent. To all intents and purposes, therefore, we can say that high-energy electrons, once they get above a few Mev, move at a *constant* velocity, namely, the velocity of light.

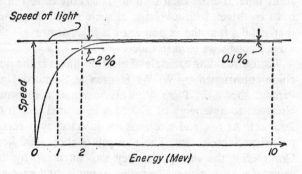

FIG. 19. *How electron speed varies with energy is shown in this graph. Energy, in millions of electron volts, is plotted on the horizontal axis, speed on the vertical axis. The upper horizontal line parallel to the energy axis is the constant speed of light, which the electron can approach but can never quite attain.*

It is not difficult to see how this approach to the universal speed limit helps in the design of an electron linac. We no longer need to make successive electrodes longer and longer. For very high energies, our machine can consist of a very large number of *identical* sections, and it is an easy step from this to the construction of a single, concertina-like electrode for the whole length of the accelerator. This continuous, ribbed electrode could be thought of as a long string of very short sections. Another way of envisaging its action is to think of the voltage traveling down the tube in a sort of tidal wave, sweeping the electrons along with it. The long, ribbed tube is in fact called a *waveguide;* the ribs make the wave travel at just the right speed. If we picture the very short gaps of which it consists, and remember that the electrons are traveling as fast as anything can go, then it will be clear that this system will need to work at a very high frequency indeed: the electrons take only a very short time to cross each section. Thus an electron linac must be driven with a voltage of such a high frequency that it falls into the region known as microwaves—the same frequencies used in radar.

The outstanding example of electron linacs is the machine constructed by W. W. Hansen at Stanford University, shown in Plate V. This machine accelerates electrons to an energy of 600 Mev in a total length of 200 feet! At one end electrons are injected by a small, pulsed pre-accelerator. Their energy is about 100 kev. On entering the waveguide, they are caught up by the wave of electric voltage traveling along it, and accelerated more and more. Very quickly they reach the speed limit, and after this point they increase in mass, not in speed. But this process only makes it easier for the electric voltage wave and the electrons to stay in step.

Preparations were being made at Stanford in 1960 for the construction of a still more powerful electron linac. According to plans, this machine will be two miles long and will accelerate electrons to an energy of the order of 50 Bev (50 *billion* electron volts). The physicists at Stanford expect this linear colossus to cost 125 million dollars—which gives one some indication of the complexity and size of the operation!

Before leaving the subject of linear accelerators, let us attempt to place them in their historical perspective. It is probably fair to say that Wideröe's original idea has had its most fruitful consequences in a different application, that of the cyclotron and its offspring. His proposal of using alternating voltages for acceleration was nothing short of visionary, and his understanding of the inherent phase stability was of the greatest importance. At the time, however, technology was not sufficiently far advanced to permit the construction of an important linear accelerator. It was not until much later that this species has come into its rights. For example, a large-scale proton linac was constructed at the University of California in 1946 by Luis Alvarez. Concurrent developments of circular machines have always overshadowed the achievements of the proton linacs.

The story is quite different for the electron linac. Here, the required microwave technology was not developed until after World War II; Hansen's accelerator, already described, became an important research tool upon its completion. While competition with circular accelerators also exists in this field, there is an important difference: circular accelerators capable of bringing electrons to extremely high energy are dogged by a certain difficulty—the electrons begin to radiate an appreciable fraction of their energy when they are constrained to move in circular orbits. Although this radiation has not crippled the development of suitable accelerators, it nevertheless presents an obstacle that becomes more and more forbidding as the energy is raised. The proposal to construct a monster electron linac to go to 50 Bev is a direct bid to bypass this difficulty altogether, and it is possible that in this extreme range of energies only the linac will be a suitable device for accelerating electrons.

But we have digressed far from the main narrative. Let us return to the more modest machines we were considering, and in particular let us prepare to introduce that most famous of all modern accelerators, Ernest O. Lawrence's cyclotron.

Chapter 5

THE CYCLOTRON

Wideröe's linear-accelerator system represented the first
penetration of the high-voltage barrier, which up to then
had limited the energies to which particles could be accelerated. However, a linac needs a long string of electrodes of carefully computed lengths, all which must
be supplied with radio-frequency power at high intensity
and with the correct timing. This system proved to be
cumbersome and difficult to put into practice. It was
Ernest O. Lawrence's brilliant idea to bend the particle

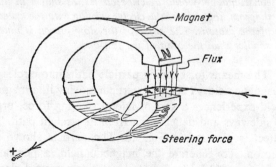

FIG. 20. *This schematic diagram shows the deflection
of a proton in a magnetic field. The magnetic force
steers the proton out of its straight path into an arc of
a circle.*

paths into *circles:* the particles then could be made to pass time and again through the *same* electrode system, and a tremendous simplification would be achieved.

Lawrence's idea worked almost like magic. His cyclotron is a marvelously successful accelerator. It is the grandfather of a large tribe of modern machines, and accelerator men pay it due reverence. The conception of the cyclotron was one of those strokes of genius which every ambitious physicist dreams about.

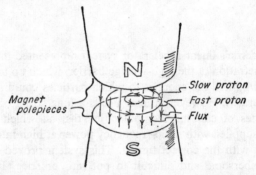

FIG. 21. *Protons traveling between the poles of a large electromagnet would describe circles, as shown in this diagram, the radii of the circles varying with the speeds of the protons. The circle of the slow proton is much smaller than the orbit of the fast one.*

The means for bending particle paths into circles is a magnetic field. A charged particle moving in a magnetic field experiences a sort of lateral steering force, urging it sideways and deflecting it from its straight path. This effect is pictured in Fig. 20. The particle shown is a proton. To generate the magnetic field, a permanent magnet could be used, but in practice powerful electromagnets are usually chosen. As the proton moves, the magnetic steering force pushes it sideways, and the proton's actual path becomes circular. For a fast-moving proton the steering is not so effective; the circle is much larger than for slow protons.

Particles in Spiral Orbits

Figure 21 shows a plan view of the region between the poles of a large electromagnet. The polefaces, shown in outline, are circular; the magnetic field fills the space between them. In the diagram the direction of the field is in and out of the paper. The orbits of two protons are indicated, one for a fast particle, the other for a slow one. (We keep talking of protons here rather than of electrons, since electrons above a few Mev can no longer be called slow and fast. They all travel with very nearly the velocity of light.) It turns out that the diameter of the circle in which a proton moves is proportional to its speed; double the speed and you also double the size of

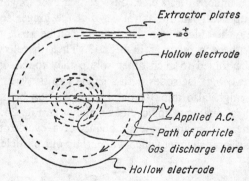

FIG. 22. *The basic plan of the cyclotron is shown in this simplified diagram. Its difference from the apparatus of Fig. 21 is the addition of the hollow electrodes, which accelerate the particles as they complete each half circle. The extractor plates are deflecting electrodes, which guide the highly accelerated particles out of the magnetic field region and aim them at an externally placed target.*

the circle. This is an extremely lucky circumstance, for it means that the *time* taken for a complete circle is fixed. The fast particles are forced to the larger circles and take just as long for a complete revolution as do the slow ones, which have the benefit of the inside track.

If we now add two hollow electrodes as shown in Fig. 22 to our apparatus and apply an alternating voltage between them, we have a cyclotron. Of course, the frequency of the voltage must be just right; it must reverse its polarity in just the time it takes for a particle to go through a half circle. Then each time the particle crosses from one electrode to the other, it will experience an acceleration. This situation is similar to the one we met in the linac system. The cyclotron has this advantage, however: it requires only two electrodes, and not a whole string of them stretching out over great distances.

You might think of the cyclotron in this way: Start with a linac, with its electrodes getting ever longer. Coil this up neatly into a spiral, so that the longer sections fit into the outer turns. All the gaps can be made to line up with each other as in Fig. 23. Then the electrodes can be joined to each other where they touch, leaving just two big electrodes with a single gap between them. You might also think through the operation of the mechanical analog of the cyclotron shown in Fig. 24.

These then are the components of a cyclotron. We need a large magnet which will curl up our particle paths

FIG. 23. *This diagram illustrates the similarity of a cyclotron to a linac coiled up in spiral form with all the gaps lined up.*

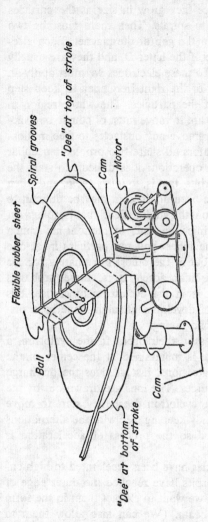

Spiral grooves

"Dee" at top of stroke

Cam

Motor

Flexible rubber sheet

Ball

Cam

"Dee" at bottom of stroke

FIG. 24. *In this mechanical analog of the cyclotron the ball undergoes acceleration each time it rolls down the sloping section joining the two movable platforms, which correspond to the accelerating electrodes of the real machine. When correctly timed, the cam mechanism raises each platform as the ball traverses the spiral groove; thus the ball conserves its speed and makes a down-hill passage at the next crossing. The operation is quite similar to that of the movable bowling-alley track shown in Fig. 15, B.*

into circles or, since they grow in size as the particles speed up, really into spirals. Then there must be two hollow electrodes in the gap of the magnet. Each electrode has the shape of the letter *D,* and they are usually called the "dees." To these electrodes we must apply an alternating voltage of the right frequency to keep step with the motion of the particles. The whole region in which the particles are to move must of course be evacuated carefully to remove any obstacles to free motion.

Circular accelerators all share two problems peculiar to their method of operation: it is difficult to start the particles on their orbits, that is, to *inject* them, and when the final energy has been attained, it may be difficult to free the particles from the guiding field, that is, to *extract* them. Obviously injection and extraction are much easier for linear machines—you put particles in at one end and get them out at the other! Fortunately for the development of circular accelerators, these problems were not too serious in the cyclotron; otherwise, this most fruitful line of development might have been discouraged from the beginning.

To start particles on their orbits in the cyclotron, a small gas discharge is maintained at the center of the machine. This creates ions, just as does the discharge in the usual ion sources. The ions are drawn out by the electric field of the cyclotron dees; they start to move in tiny circles, already keeping step with the alternations of the voltage, and so the process of acceleration is under way.

When the particles have been accelerated to high energies, and their orbits have reached the outer edge of the magnetic field, we want to extract them in the form of a manageable beam. (We can also allow them to collide with our "targets" inside the machine itself, but this is less controllable and precise.) In the cyclotron the particle orbits are essentially spirals, with successive turns separated by a distance corresponding to the acceleration received in one complete revolution. The end of the spiral can be made to lead into a channel, where a deflecting electrode bends the trajectories out of the magnet gap. Once out of the field region, the particles travel in straight lines, of course: this gives us our extracted beam. Since some of the particles inevitably collide with the deflecting electrode and are thus lost, the extracted (or external) beam is generally somewhat less intense than the beam circulating within the machine.

When Lawrence had hit upon the cyclotron idea, he set to work with relentless energy to construct a model of the machine. Working in collaboration with M. Stanley Livingston, now at M.I.T., he constructed a small model machine, at first only 4″ in diameter, with which he was able to accelerate hydrogen ions to an energy of 13 kev. Although 13 kev established no record of particle energy, it convincingly demonstrated the soundness of the principle; from this point on success followed upon success, and ever larger machines were built and brought into operation. The first cyclotron to produce an artificial nuclear disintegration was an 11″ model, capable of producing 1.2 Mev protons. This machine made its debut in nuclear physics in October 1932, only a few months after the first artificial disintegration had been announced by Cockroft and Walton. Plates VI and VII show the 11″ cyclotron and its associated controls; in those days simple apparatus and primitive methods were used. It is amusing to follow the progress of technology as illustrated in the succession of bigger cyclotrons built by Lawrence at Berkeley. In Plate VIII we see the next machine, a 27″ cyclotron, which could accelerate ions of heavy hydrogen to 5 Mev. This machine already has a slightly more professional look, but its control table (Plate IX) still smacks of haywire, and amusing anecdotes are told about the machine by the men who worked with it. Livingston recounts how the magnet coils, which were cooled by immersion in oil, used to leak, and everyone working close by had to wear a paper hat to keep the oil out of his hair!

A view of an improved vacuum tank for this 27″ machine is shown in Plate VI. Here, we can clearly see the accelerating dees, as well as a sort of hairpin wire near the center which was used for maintaining the source arc. Plate IX shows the extracted beam of particles from this cyclotron. With the room lights out, the glow of the air caused by the passage of the fast particles looks very impressive and eerie.

Phase and Frequency

After this historical interlude, let us go back to the operation of the cyclotron and some of its limiting features. The first point to make is a rather surprising one: phase stability (see Chapter 4) does not exist in the cyclotron. True, the machine uses the same principles of acceleration as Wideröe's linac; but the fact that the particles travel on circular orbits introduces an important change. We have seen how the fast particles, traveling on correspondingly large orbits, take the same time for their revolutions as the slower ones. Otherwise it would be impossible, of course, for the *same* pair of electrodes to accelerate simultaneously particles of *different* velocities. But this result also excludes the self-regulating feature that led to phase stability. A fast particle will *not* arrive too soon at the gap, nor a slow one too late. They all arrive at times which are independent of their energy: phase stability does not exist.

Fortunately, lack of phase stability does not ruin the operation of the machine. It just means that some particles receive big kicks at each traversal, and others receive small ones. The spiral of the lucky particles opens very rapidly as they gain energy. The unlucky ones have to make many, many turns to gain the same total energy; their spirals will be tightly wound and very long. Of course, the time taken for full acceleration cannot, in practice, be arbitrarily long. Imagine a proton's spending years going around and around in our machine, just because it happens to be moving at a slow phase! This proton is a poor bet to reach the outside track at all. It spends so long in the machine that it probably will meet violent death—for instance, in colliding with a residual gas atom still roaming about in the cyclotron. More important would be the proton's problem of keeping in step with the accelerating voltage for such a long period of time. In principle the particle stays in step all along, but in fact the magnetic field is not quite uniform, and for this and other reasons the phase will change during the acceleration, which may either improve or worsen the performance. Even a slight error in the frequency, however, would accumulate rapidly and would ultimately cause our proton to be decelerated at the crossings.

Since there is no phase stability in the cyclotron, the frequency we apply must be made precise. Take the following example. A small cyclotron is expected to accelerate protons to 5 Mev, and the maximum voltage applied to the dees is 50 kv. For each turn, the proton receives two accelerations, each at most 50 kv. We assume that on the average it gets only a half-maximum push, so that per turn we have an energy gain of 50 kev. Thus one hundred turns would be needed to reach an energy of 5 Mev. This tells us that the proton and the driving voltage must remain nicely in step for at least one hundred turns. If you reflect for a moment, you will see that this demands a frequency correct to better than 1 per cent.

To accelerate particles traveling at a less favorable

phase would need even greater precision, of course.
These particles receive smaller accelerations on each
turn, take longer to reach the final energy, and thus
impose more stringent requirements on the frequency
match. So we see that the output intensity of the machine will be greatest if the frequency is absolutely correct; then even particles at very unfavorable phases can
be accelerated. As the frequency is changed from this
optimum value on either side, the intensity will fall off.
This relationship between beam intensity and frequency
is shown in Fig. 25. The shape of the curve—a sharp
peak with a "skirt" on either side—is known as a resonance shape, since it is characteristic of all processes
that involve keeping in step with a periodic process—
that is, staying in resonance. The cyclotron principle of
acceleration is often called the *resonance principle.*

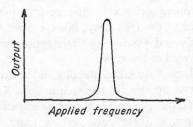

FIG. 25.   *This curve, which shows the relationship between beam intensity and frequency, has the resonance
shape, a sharp peak with a "skirt" at either side. It is
characteristic of phenomena that have to keep in step
with a periodic process.*

Energy Limits of the Cyclotron

Now we are ready to consider why there is an upper
limit to the energy achievable with a cyclotron. Again
we run into the effects of Relativity. The operation of
the cyclotron relies entirely on the fact that the particles

take the same time to make their turns whether they move fast or slowly. If this were not so, then resonance could not be maintained, since there is no helpful phase stability. From the equivalence of mass and energy, we have seen that particles get heavier as they gain energy. But particles of *different* mass do *not* take the same time; a heavy particle takes longer. So once the relativistic increase of mass becomes noticeable, the resonance situation in the cyclotron is upset.

The effects of Relativity become noticeable as soon as the energy we have given to the particle is no longer insignificant compared with the particle's inherent rest-energy. The mass of a proton (which is about 2000 times heavier than the electron) corresponds to an energy of about 1000 Mev. Thus every proton has this high energy tucked away in its mass. If we accelerate the proton to 10 Mev, its *total* energy will now be 1010 Mev, or we will have made a change of 1 per cent. For this reason, a 10-Mev proton is 1 per cent heavier than a proton at rest. So to make a significant change in the mass of a proton, we must accelerate it to energies of at least 10 Mev. This contrasts with the case of the electron, where the mass had already been doubled at 0.5 Mev! It also explains why electrons are not used in ordinary cyclotrons—their mass is much too easily changed. In practice, the relativistic increase of the proton mass makes it hard to construct cyclotrons for energies above about 25 Mev; but heavier particles—for example, deuterons or alpha particles—can be accelerated to higher energies.

It is typical of the aggressive spirit of research physicists that, despite these limitations on the energy of a conventional cyclotron, plans were made for the construction of a much bigger machine at Berkeley. Just how this would work was never quite clear, for it involved the use of enormous voltages on the cyclotron dees. Lawrence hoped by this means to accelerate the particles so rapidly that their relativistic mass increase would not prove too crippling. (The rest of this story is told in Chapter 8, so we will not anticipate the point here.) However, if you want to appreciate this kind of daredevil approach, you must enter a little into the spirit in which accelerators are built.

Lawrence and the California Radiation Lab

When one of the authors of this book was a freshman at the University of California in 1932, he had to pass a ramshackle old wooden building on his way to a chemistry laboratory course. He remembers the whining noise of generators, the crackling of sparks, the brilliantly beautiful glow of mercury-arc rectifiers, strange shiny instruments, the fevered activity of men in laboratory coats moving rapidly in and out of the deep shadows caused by the eerie light; all this fascinated him. Every day watching this mysterious drama made him late for his lab course. As he stood there one day, nose pressed to the window glass, oblivious to a pouring rain, a compassionate scientist invited him in out of the wet. If there is anything that can bind two strangers together it is a common interest, and soon the two were deep in conversation; the older man, no doubt animated by the student's interest, explained the complicated equipment, demonstrated how some of it worked, indicated the underlying principles, conveyed the excitement and deep satisfaction of the explorations of the nucleus that were going on there. He even expounded the philosophical and social possibilities of the new knowledge. The old wooden building was the Radiation Laboratory, and its wonders trapped the young man for life.

The central activity in the Radiation Laboratory was

the construction of the cyclotron. The electromagnet seemed huge—it weighed 85 tons—and had originally been slated for use in China as a Poulsen-arc generator of radio waves. The method was already obsolete, so the generator had been lying in a storehouse, unused and unpaid for. It had come to the laboratory as a gift. This was characteristic; nearly everything was second-hand or had been "scrounged" from some factory or dump yard. Not infrequently the electronic equipment was obtained by taking discarded radios apart. Most of the mechanical parts were handmade in the small shop, and usually the physicists themselves turned out the parts on an old lathe. The vacuum chamber was a joy to behold. It was made by screwing brass sides to the poletips of the magnet polepieces. The whole thing was then made vacuum-tight by heating the metal with a gas torch and painting a hot, smelly, smoking mixture of beeswax and rosin over the surface. Needless to say, the physicists spent most of their time trying to make this system vacuum-tight. The oil pumps were homemade, the radio-frequency oscillator tubes were homemade. In fact, almost everything was makeshift and uniquely designed for just one purpose—to make that miserable cyclotron work at a minimum outlay of money and—what was more valuable—of the physicists' time. This sort of activity at a university has always been a part-time occupation. The senior people were professors and always had to hurry off to a lecture or to attend a faculty committee meeting. The others were mostly students who supported themselves as teaching assistants and were fully occupied by their course work. It was not strange then that most of the work got done late at night. Not at all unusual was it to break up at 4 A.M. for a cup of coffee at the all-night White Tavern or, if earlier, for a bit of camaraderie at the Anchor over a glass of beer and an abalone sandwich. Central to all this was the personality of Ernest Lawrence, The Maestro, as he was affectionately called in those days. His own hard work established the quick pace. We didn't walk in the lab—everything was done at a dead run. His encouraging optimism kept us focused on our successes, not our dismal failures. His physical insight and intuition commanded respect, for his suggestions invariably were useful. Yet he did not dominate the scene, and every worker in that laboratory had the satisfaction of developing ideas and theories of his own.

As larger and larger cyclotrons were built, Lawrence was more and more successful in raising money for building yet larger machines. Now the physicists' real motive in building the machines was to *use* them as instruments for investigating the properties of the nucleus, and this they did. Thus, as larger machines were built, it was feasible and even necessary to obtain engineering help. Furthermore, science and technology go hand in hand, and the technologies of electronics, radio oscillators, and pumping techniques were advancing apace. Especially during World War II, when the efforts of the laboratory were turned from the study of the nucleus to the development of methods of purifying the explosive isotope of uranium, large amounts of money, large numbers of engineers, and a wealth of technological commercial equipment were made available. The laboratory became a thriving industry with several thousands of employees. It is interesting to compare the slick engineering practices of the great modern Lawrence Radiation Laboratory of today with the amateur efforts of the old wooden Radiation Laboratory that has long since been torn down. The results of the new laboratory are impressive, however nostalgic one wants to be for the "good old days." The nuclear physicist is now more purely occupied in doing those things for which he has been uniquely trained and, although it may be less fun, it is surely more efficient and more productive.

There is a story about Lawrence, no doubt apocryphal, that illustrates one of the frustrating disadvantages of bigness. In the huge modern organization Lawrence could not possibly know everyone, but it was still his custom to visit all parts of the laboratory and to expect the research worker at a particular piece of equipment to explain to him the progress being made or at least to have ready a good discussion of the difficulties encountered. One day Lawrence bustled up to the complicated control desk of the linear accelerator. Instead of finding the usual eager-faced young research student flattered at the attention of "the boss," he came upon a blasé young man, feet on the table, who was busily reading a lurid paperback.

"Tell me what's going on," ordered Lawrence. "How is the beam?"

Without removing his feet from the table or raising his eyes, the young man said, "I haven't the foggiest idea."

"Well, that's no attitude to have in this laboratory," rasped out Lawrence. "In fact, you're fired."

"You can't fire me," drawled the indolent one.

"And why not?" said Lawrence, drawing himself up. "I'm the director of this laboratory."

"Because I work for the Telephone Company."

Chapter 6

THE BETATRON

So far in our story of the evolution of high-energy accelerators we have seen the cyclotron as an enormously successful species in its own right, and later on we shall consider its role in the development of other modern machines. But first we must digress a bit to study a specialized offshoot, the betatron. It operates on an entirely different principle, and the crossing of some of its features with those of the cyclotron has been fruitful in producing several types of modern accelerator.

You will recall from Chapter 3 that some radioactive substances in the process of decay emit beta rays, which analysis eventually identified as high-speed electrons, but which are still known by their original name in some contexts. The name betatron implies, obviously, that this accelerator was designed specifically for electrons.

A German physicist, M. Steinbeck, was the first to come on the betatron principle, and he obtained a patent in 1936, but D. W. Kerst, an American, built the first practical machine in 1939. The betatron is an induction machine, operating much as a transformer does. As you will recall from Chapter 2, in a transformer a changing magnetic flux induces a voltage in the turns of wire wrapped around it, and the greater the number of turns, all connected in series, the higher the total resulting voltage. The high-voltage breakdown that always plagues such devices limits the attainable voltage.

Electrons in Circular Orbits

Suppose, however, that instead of wrapping many turns of wire around our magnetic core, we persuade a bundle of electrons to circle the core repeatedly. Every time an electron completes one turn around the magnet, it will have experienced an acceleration equal to the voltage induced in one turn of wire. Let the electron make a thousand turns, and it will gain a thousand times the energy. The beauty of the scheme lies in the fact that nowhere does the total high voltage appear directly to threaten a breakdown of insulation. Since there are no actual turns of wire connected in series, no voltages are added up. Only the electrons making many successive turns perform this addition, and they accumulate energy in ever increasing amounts. Thus the betatron is simply a transformer having standard primary turns, the secondary turns being made by the electrons moving around the core.

To make such a scheme practicable, we must have a means of holding the electrons in circular orbits for many thousands of revolutions. This is the function of the *guide field,* a magnetic field rather like that in a cyclotron, which deflects the charged electrons from their straight paths into circular ones. However, in the betatron the orbits must enclose a changing magnetic flux in an iron core if acceleration is to be achieved. Therefore very small orbits are not possible. The practice is to try to keep the orbit radius constant, independent of electron energy. This is where the betatron differs from the cyclotron. In the cyclotron the orbits begin as tight little curls when the particles have low energy, and they unfold and become larger and larger as the energy of the particles builds up. In the betatron, on the other hand, the orbit radius stays constant, or as nearly constant as we can manage. The strength of the magnetic field must vary. We need a weak field to guide the particles at low energy and a stronger and stronger field to hold the radius as the energy increases.

We can state this very important difference in another way. The guide fields in both machines must handle particles over a wide range of energies, starting with the initial low energy and going all the way up to the final high energy. The cyclotron does the job with a *constant* magnetic field by letting the orbit radius increase. The betatron keeps the orbit radius fixed but changes the magnetic-field strength as the energy of the particles builds up. The cyclotron guide field covers a whole disk-shaped region through which the electrons travel, but the betatron needs only an outer ring-shaped guide field.

In a changing magnetic guide field only particles of one specific energy can be present at any instant. As the guide field varies cyclically, then, the particles go from low to high energy in the same rhythm, and the betatron works like a reciprocating pump or, a better analogy, like an elevator. It goes up and down, picking up and carrying passengers in groups. On the other hand, the cyclotron works like an escalator, or moving staircase. Its passengers ride on all levels simultaneously and arrive at the top in a continuous stream, not in groups.

Two Magnetic Fields

To make the betatron work, we need two kinds of magnetic field. First, we need the changing flux at the center of the orbits to give the electrons a continuous push by a sort of transformer action. Second, we need the guide field to hold the electrons in circular paths surrounding the accelerating flux. Figure 26 shows the betatron arrangement. The guide field must vary in such a way as to keep in step with the rising energy of the electrons. It turns out that maintaining synchronism of the two fields is not much of a problem. In fact, both fields have to change in an entirely parallel manner. If we design polepieces rather like the ones shown in Fig. 26, then the correct tracking follows automatically. The electrons travel in an evacuated tube in the region of the guide field, as shown, while the magnetic flux going through the center of the orbits has been chosen to provide the right amount of acceleration. Apply alternating current to the coils of such an electromagnet and you have the elements of the betatron.

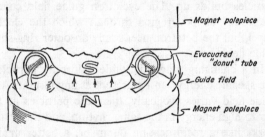

FIG. 26. *The betatron, as shown in this schematic drawing, consists of electromagnetic polepieces to produce the changing flux that accelerates the electrons and the evacuated circular tube in which the electrons travel in a guide field. The accelerating flux and the guide field must vary in synchronism.*

Figure 27 shows the time variations of the magnetic fields in the betatron. If we apply ordinary A.C., the fields vary periodically from one direction to the other. When the field has a small instantaneous value in the desired direction for bending electrons, such as at point *A* on the diagram, we inject a burst of electrons of the right energy. (Just how this can be done will be described in a moment.) These electrons travel in the guide field at just the right radius to make repeated trips around the central accelerating flux. As they do so, they start to gain energy by transformer action, since the central flux is changing. At the same time, the guide field also increases correspondingly, and the electrons remain on their correct orbits. The magnetic fields continue to build up to a maximum, at point *B*. At this instant, the electrons have reached the highest energy, and they must now be caught and used for whatever experiments they were intended. Afterward, the magnetic field completes the cycle, a new burst of electrons is injected at time *A'*, and in this manner the machine continues its pulsating action.

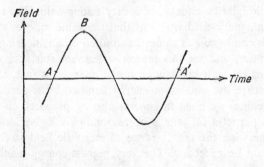

FIG. 27. *Variation of the betatron magnetic fields with time is plotted in this graph. The electrons are injected at* A; *at* B *they have reached peak energy. New cycle starts at* A'.

Injection and Extraction

Because of the reciprocating action of the betatron, injection of electrons into its working space is a rather delicate matter. A burst, or pulse, of electrons must en-

ter at just the right time and at just the right energy if
the particles are to start off correctly. They must make
their first trip around the guide field like fully seasoned
accelerator travelers—no breaking in or warming up
allowed! So we shall use a pulsed electron gun of relatively high energy as our injector. For example, in a
betatron capable of accelerating electrons to 50 Mev,
we might inject at an initial energy of 100 kev. Thus
even the injection process requires relatively quite high
energies, a feature common to many of the reciprocating
or pulsed accelerators. The reason for this is practical.
The magnetic field at injection time (points A and A'
in Fig. 27) is quite weak by comparison with the maximum field that will ultimately be reached. Now, it is
very hard to design a magnet that will produce a very
weak field of just the right proportions and a little
while later be capable of a very strong field. The range
of magnetic-field strengths that the same magnet structure can handle is somewhat limited by engineering difficulties, and for this reason we cannot start our electrons off with too low an initial energy. In fact, as we
increase the maximum energy handled by a particular
machine, we must in general also be prepared to start
the particles off with a correspondingly higher energy.
Otherwise, the usable range of magnetic field strengths
would be exceeded. The very highest-energy machines
usually feed on smaller ones, and sometimes the injectors themselves have their own injectors.

The electron guns for injecting electrons into betatrons
are usually of a very simple design (Fig. 28). The principle is the same as for electron guns in television
tubes,* except that for injection purposes only pulsed
operation for repeated very short intervals of time is
desired. On the other hand, relatively high electron cur-

* See *The Physics of Television,* by Donald G. Fink and David
M. Lutyens (Science Study Series).

rents are needed during those short bursts. The gun is therefore designed for high currents, but the problems of insulation are not so severe, since the high voltage is maintained only for a very brief time, perhaps a few millionths of a second. The brief duration reduces the chance of breakdown in the high-voltage pulse. The source of high voltage is usually a special transformer (a *pulse* transformer) actuated by an electronic switching tube of very fast response. The whole gun structure is placed inside the vacuum chamber of the betatron, just outside the desired orbit location. The electrons are then injected tangentially into their initial orbits.

How to get at the accelerated electrons after the machine's cycle has reached its peak is another problem. As we have seen, *injection* and *extraction* of particles present particular difficulties with circular machines. In the betatron, or any accelerator in which the particles travel on orbits of constant radius, these difficulties are accentuated. Think of the cyclotron, for example. Here the particle trajectories are spirals, and it is not too difficult to make the end of a spiral point into some extraction device like a pair of deflector plates; the particles will be withdrawn automatically from the guide field when they reach a certain radius. In the betatron, on the other hand, the radius does not change during acceleration. Moreover, it would be difficult to make it change deliberately at the end of the acceleration cycle; in general, such induced changes happen too slowly to allow the particles to enter a deflection system without first striking the deflector plates themselves. So we must resort to rather more complicated stratagems.

From Electrons to X-Rays

Fortunately, many betatron experiments have been concerned with high-energy X-rays rather than with the electrons. X-rays, you will remember, are generated whenever fast electrons strike an obstacle. This is exactly parallel to the functioning of an X-ray tube. Now, it is quite easy to make the electrons strike an *internally* placed obstacle in the betatron as indicated in Fig. 28. All one has to do is to change the orbit radius at the end of the acceleration cycle—for example, by disturbing the balance of the magnetic fields a little. Then the

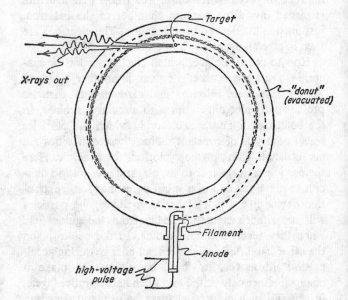

FIG. 28. *Generating X-rays is a comparatively simple business in the betatron. Electrons, injected from the electron gun at the bottom of the diagram, travel around the circular evacuated tube. If, after acceleration, the magnetic-field balance is disturbed, the radius of the electron orbit changes, and the electrons strike the target, which has been placed in the tube. When accelerated electrons strike an obstacle (the target), X-rays are generated.*

electrons gradually will expand or shrink their orbits, and strike obstacles (or *targets*) placed within the machine. Here they generate the X-rays. The X-rays are not deflected by the magnetic guide fields, since they are not electrically charged, and hence they will emerge tangentially from the machine and can then be employed for external experimentation. Some lower-energy betatrons have been used in this manner to generate X-rays for industrial or medical purposes. The higher-energy machines are generally reserved for experiments in nuclear and particle physics.

Dr. Kerst's first betatron, built in 1939, was a small model, reaching an energy of only 2.5 Mev. There are now much larger machines. The biggest, built by Kerst at the University of Illinois, accelerates to 312 Mev. Beyond this size the betatron becomes progressively less economical. The amounts of magnetic flux needed to accelerate the electrons to still higher energies can be obtained only with magnets of enormous cross section, and they would eat up power.

At high energies an interesting effect begins to appear when a guide field deflects electrons into circular orbits. The steering force which the electrons experience urges them toward the center of the machine and thus into curved instead of straight paths. But this continual deflection corresponds to a lateral acceleration of the particles, and an electron which is accelerated (or decelerated) radiates electromagnetic waves. (For instance, if the electrons strike an obstacle, they are decelerated rapidly, and they radiate X-rays, which are electromagnetic waves.) The radial acceleration from the guide field is not so drastic, and the generated waves are less energetic than X-rays, but the higher the energy of the electrons, and the more tightly curved their paths, the more radiation occurs. This effect is known as *synchrotron radiation,* because it was observed first in a different machine, the synchrotron. It is present, however, whenever electrons are guided into circular paths.

The amount of synchrotron radiation increases very rapidly as the energy of the electrons rises. On an orbit of constant radius, the radiation given out per turn goes up by a factor of 16 whenever the energy is doubled! At low energies the synchrotron radiation is mostly in the form of radio waves, and of negligible quantity. As we make more and more powerful electron accelerators, however, the radiation increases in importance. Soon it appears in the form of visible light, and ultimately it extends into the region of the ultraviolet, or even to soft X-rays. At the same time, it imposes an energy loss on the circulating electrons; a "tax" has to be paid for the privilege of deflecting them with a guide field. This tax upsets the energy balance of the betatron, and the accelerating field has to be made more powerful to keep step with the rising guide field—now we must not only accelerate the electrons according to schedule, but also make up for the energy loss given out as synchrotron radiation. The energy tax rises drastically as the electron energy goes up; soon the betatron action becomes very difficult to maintain in balance.

Focusing and Orbital Stability

We now have met two examples of accelerators which use magnetic guide fields to steer their particles into circular paths, the cyclotron and the betatron. The guide field is the traffic lane of our accelerator, and on successful design and layout of the field depends the successful operation of the machine. Let us pause for a moment to examine this traffic lane in some detail, for our particles have to make many trips along it, and we must try to keep traffic fatalities to a minimum. As a matter of fact, in some accelerators the distance traveled from source to target can be as much as ten thousand miles.

The most important function of the guide field is, of course, the correct steering of the particles. But correct steering is not in itself enough. Picture a driver about to put his car through a speed trial on a circular race track. He might set the steering wheel at the correct angle and lock it, arguing that this will be just right to make the car travel on the track for ever and ever. This won't work, and we all know why. There are always small disturbances which will deflect the car from its expected course, and we must continually be ready to compensate for these little errors. If the steering wheel is locked, nothing can be done about the deviations, and pretty soon the car will go off the track and crash.

Unfortunately, we cannot build a skilled driver into each of the particles we hope to accelerate. Any compensation for error must therefore be made from the outside, from the track rather than from the car. To picture this more vividly, we might change the analogy and talk of simple bobsleds on a banked curve; we assume that the sled has no means of steering at all. The only way the sled can make the turn is to ride up on the bank and be steered by it. Such a situation is shown in Fig. 29, where a uniformly banked curve is sketched at *A* and a graduated one at *B*. A sled can negotiate curve *A* only at precisely the right speed. If it travels too slowly, it will slip toward the inside and cannot recover; if it goes too fast, it will fly off on the outside. Curve *B* is more tolerant. Let the sled go a little too fast and it will ride toward the outside as before, but now the bank gets steeper, and pretty soon the sled finds a level at which it can make the curve in comfort. In the same way a sled that goes too slowly will drop toward the inside, where the banking is less steep.

There is an easy and instructive experiment you can

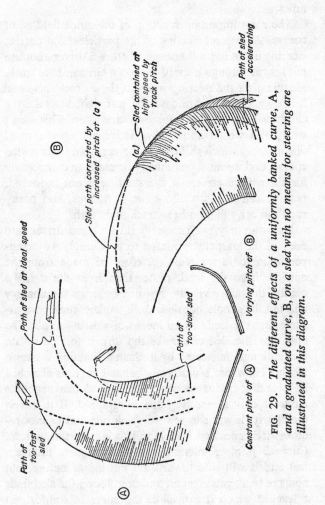

FIG. 29. The different effects of a uniformly banked curve, A, and a graduated curve, B, on a sled with no means for steering are illustrated in this diagram.

perform to help you visualize this sort of externally steered motion around a curve. Take a shallow bowl, preferably round, not oval. A round wooden salad bowl is suitable. In this bowl a ball bearing or marble can be made to revolve at various levels. Depending on how fast you start the ball, it will negotiate the circle in different ways. You will notice at once that the trajectory is not as simple as one might expect; often the ball swings up and down rhythmically. Only if you happen to start it just right can you make it travel on a fairly smooth curve. This illustrates a property common to most self-regulating systems: they frequently overshoot the mark, and instead of a smooth correction we have an oscillatory motion.

The particles in our magnetic guide field move in ways very similar to the ball's rolling in a bowl. The fields are so laid out that they compensate for slight errors in the trajectories of the particles. Instead of reaching the equilibrium trajectory smoothly, however, particles that deviate perform oscillations around this equilibrium path. These oscillations were first studied extensively in connection with the design of betatrons. For this reason, they are usually called *betatron oscillations,* although they occur in all other accelerators using magnetic guide fields. Usually, the betatron oscillations die down slowly—we say they are *damped*—during the course of the acceleration.

In our accelerator, the strength of the field, like the banked curve *B,* must be graduated. The problem for particles in accelerators is more complicated, for we must correct not only for deviations toward the inside or outside of the track but also for displacements in the *vertical* direction. (Bobsleds, fortunately, do not fly or travel underground!) If the guide field is suitably shaped, corrections for errors in both directions can be produced. When we make these corrections, we say that there is *focusing* in both the radial and vertical directions. The use of the word "focusing" describes the action quite graphically—particles that deviate from the designed path are brought back to it at a later point, just as light rays diverging from a source are brought together at the focus of a camera's lens.

To analyze in detail what shape the magnetic field must have to perform this focusing as well as its normal steering task would take us very far afield at this point. We shall return to these questions later, however, when we discuss some of the modern inventions that produce excellent focusing.

Chapter 7

THE ELECTRON SYNCHROTRON

Nuclear physicists have been almost as inventive in naming their machines as they have been in designing them, but this play of imagination tends to baffle the layman. Who can tell a cyclotron from a synchrotron or a synchro-cyclotron? What about the Cosmotron, Bevatron, and synchroclash? The more powerful the machine, the more monstrous, or poetic, the name, depending on your point of view. Happily, there is a saving grace. The principles of operation are all about the same. Once we have a grasp of the few basic ideas underlying them all, we can shuffle the components around and get a different kind of machine in every new deal.

A good example of this reshuffling is the electron synchrotron, the idea of which occurred in 1944 to V. Veksler in Russia and independently about a year later to E. M. McMillan, then at the Los Alamos Laboratory in New Mexico. The synchrotron combines the accelerating system of the eminently successful cyclotron with the ring-shaped, pulsating guide field of the betatron. The radio-frequency accelerating system is vastly superior to the bulky (and expensive) flux core of the betatron, while the ring-shaped guide field of the latter offers economy in the construction of large machines.

Phase stability, the principle we met earlier in this book, holds the clue to the benefits derived from radio-frequency acceleration. Phase stability, you will recall, keeps the particles in a linear accelerator in step with the electric fields pushing the particles. Let us see how the principle might apply to a circular machine.

Traffic Problems

The motion of particles in the guide field of a circular accelerator can be compared with the movement of traffic around a circular road. The cars keep coming around time and again, the faster ones at shorter intervals than the slow ones. Imagine a policeman stationed at one intersection of this road, holding up traffic from time to time and then waving the cars on again. If he does this in a regular rhythm, say twice every minute, the drivers will be able to find some suitable speed at which they can travel without ever having to stop. They must take just long enough for the trip around the road so that the policeman can have completed one of his cycles of start and stop. (They could also let him go through two, three, or more complete cycles, but that will not affect our argument now.) If the road is a quarter mile long, it will take just half a minute for a car to make the loop if it moves at 30 miles per hour. Since the policeman also takes half a minute for his changes, the car can keep going at this speed indefinitely once it has found favorable timing, or a good *phase*. In fact, if all the cars move at the same speed, they will bunch until they travel more or less together, and a pedestrian at an opposite point of the loop will be able to cross quite safely between these bunches. We all have observed this kind of traffic bunching by traffic lights, and may even have made use of it for jaywalking in the middle of a block.

Now suppose one of the cars slows up a little by accident. It will arrive a little later each time it comes to the policeman and soon will find itself at the tail end of the bunch. If the policeman is ambitious, he will wave the car on, urging it to speed up and get across before he stops the traffic. If he looks fierce enough, the driver may even wake up and accelerate, ultimately recapturing his place in the traffic bunch. Similarly, a driver going too fast will soon arrive very early and collect an angry glare from the policeman for speeding. The policeman's disapproval will slow him down (if he respects the law), and he will fall back into place. Here we have a situation, then, for correcting small deviations automatically; the bunching effect is stable. This is nothing other than an example of phase stability.

What happens if the policeman changes his rhythm and, for example, slows up his cycles of stop and go? Then *all* the cars will arrive too soon and be held up by him. Ultimately, the drivers will find a lower speed at which they can keep in step. If, on the other hand, the policeman gets nervous and starts to move faster, he will wave all the cars along, and they will speed up accordingly. Thus our policeman controls the traffic quite dictatorially (not an unusual situation).

We might try to carry matters to an extreme and have our policeman get faster and faster all along. At first, the cars can keep up, although the pace of the traffic is increasing dangerously. Soon there comes a point, however, when the cars just cannot manage to go any faster. They either break down, or maybe they run over the policeman. In any case, his traffic directions become useless, for he is asking the cars to do something they just cannot comply with. This is why the policeman's manual tells him never to ask traffic to do anything unreasonable, and it is the only limitation on his important powers.

Policing the Particles

All this is fantasy, of course, but it can illuminate the principle of the circular accelerator in which a radio-frequency electrode is placed at one point on the orbit. We have seen how particles can gain energy from such an electrode if they arrive at the right time with respect to the variations of the voltage. If, on the other hand, they arrive at the wrong part of the cycle, they will gain less energy or even have to give up some. The RF electrode is directing the traffic of particles around the machine. The comparison cannot be expected to be exact, but details are of no great interest here and do not affect our conclusions. Like the policeman, the electrode must keep up a rhythm the particles are *capable* of following. So long as this restriction is observed—some particles are very inflexible about their times of revolution and hard to deal with—so long as synchronism is possible, then, the RF electrode will bunch the particles and impose its frequency upon them.

Accelerators making use of this forced synchronism are called synchrotrons, or else they may have names obviously related, like synchro-cyclotron; in this application, phase stability is often called the synchrotron principle.

The first people to exploit the principle were the betatron builders, who were only too happy to get rid of the bulky magnetic accelerating system. For them the operation was an easy one. If you use electrons, you will be getting close to the velocity of light at relatively low energies, because electrons are such light particles. It takes only a few Mev to accelerate them to within a very small margin of the velocity of light. Above this

PLATE IX. Ernest O. Lawrence at the controls of the 27-inch cyclotron is seen in the upper picture, and the machine's emerging accelerated beam in the lower picture. Collision of the accelerated particles with air molecules causes the glow.

PLATE x. While Ernest O. Lawrence and his group went on to build a 60-inch machine at California, Dr. M. Stanley Livingston (at left) moved to M.I.T. and built the 15-Mev cyclotron, which he and Dr. John H. Buck (right) are inspecting. Concrete shielding

PLATE XI. The 1.3-Bev electron synchrotron at Cornell University is shown here as it looked when the guiding magnet was being built. Van de Graaff injector, hanging from overhead rail, is visible at upper right.

PLATE XII. This 184-inch synchro-cyclotron built by Ernest O. Lawrence's group illustrates the awesome growth the science and art of atom smashing have achieved since his original device (Plate VI).

PLATE XIII. The Cosmotron at the Brookhaven National Laboratory, Upton, Long Island, is a monster machine that has a 3-million-volt Van de Graaff generator (lower left) as an injector. The Van de Graaff accelerates particles before they are introduced into the Cosmotron accelerating tube, a relatively small "donut" contained within the 288 steel blocks of the magnets.

PLATE XIV. The Lawrence Radiation Laboratory Bevatron. This proton synchrotron, which achieves 6 Bev, first permitted the creation of anti-protons in the laboratory.

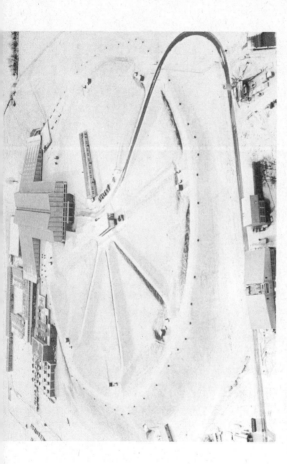

PLATE XV. This 30-Bev (Gev) accelerator outside Geneva, Switzerland, is the joint creation of the nine European nations that have formed the nuclear research center called CERN. The underground machine, which went into operation in February 1960, has a 50-Mev linac as a pre-accelerator.

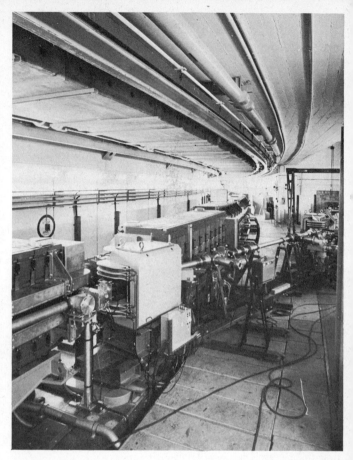

PLATE XVI. This scene inside the 2000-foot-circumference tunnel for the CERN accelerator (see aerial view, Plate XV) shows where protons are injected into the circular track. The machine at the right is the 50-Mev linear accelerator.

energy the electrons can for practical purposes be considered as moving at constant speed. (Add more energy, and they just get heavier.) The traffic-control problem is thus a simple one: maintain a constant frequency corresponding to the constant speed of the electrons and the desired length of their orbit.

But how can the synchrotron principle work if the electrons travel at *constant* speed? Electrons at different energies may have the same velocity, but their bending in a magnetic guide field will be different. The higher-energy (heavier) particle will be harder to deflect, and in a given guide field will travel on a larger circle than the lower-energy one. Thus the length of the orbit depends on the energy, and the time of arrival at the RF electrode will vary in spite of the constant velocity. Phase stability is therefore present. It will always adjust the electron energy to maintain the orbit radius at the desired value.

Let us start the electrons in the synchrotron at an energy of a few Mev, for example by pre-accelerating them in a Van de Graaff machine. As they enter the synchrotron, its guide field must have a suitable strength to bend them into the prescribed orbit. Then the RF electrode will maintain this orbit, even if minor fluctuations in the electron energy should occur. Now we increase the strength of the guide field very slowly. At first the electron paths will be bent into smaller circles, but the synchrotron principle will immediately restore them to proper radius. In the process they gain just the right amount of energy from the RF electrode. As the guide field increases more and more, the electron energy builds up, always keeping in step automatically. Finally, with the guide field at its strongest, we may have electrons of very high energy which we can use for research or other purposes. The final energy bears the same relationship to the initial energy as does the final guide field to the initial. This ratio can be made very large—for example, a factor of 500. Then if we start with 2 Mev electrons, we will attain 1000 Mev, or 1 Bev—a billion electron volts—at the end!

The synchrotron acts in a pulsating manner, just as the betatron does. This is a necessary price we must pay for keeping the orbit radius constant. Something has to vary as the particles gain energy, and it can be either the orbit radius (as in the cyclotron) or the strength of the guide field, as here. The synchrotron differs from the betatron in one very important respect, apart from its much less bulky and less costly accelerating system. It is a tolerant machine. The particle energy adjusts itself automatically to keep in step with the guide field, whereas in the betatron a sort of dead reckoning had to be used to provide just the right amount of acceleration at each instant. So the synchrotron can adjust itself to all sorts of slight disturbances, most important of which is the energy loss by radiation as the electrons attain very high energy. This "energy tax," which we described previously, turned out to be the chief limiting factor on the energy of betatrons. For the synchrotron, the radiation loss is of no consequence, provided it is not so large as to exceed the maximum energy that can be gained from the RF electrode.

As we have said, the conversion of a betatron to synchrotron operation is a relatively easy matter. Not long after Veksler and McMillan had pointed out the principle, F. K. Goward and D. E. Barnes had a machine in operation in England. Then a 50-Mev betatron at the General Electric Research Laboratory, in Schenectady, was converted to a 70-Mev synchrotron. The principle worked just as predicted and with amazing ease and elegance. The marriage of RF acceleration and ring-shaped orbits was a happy one from the start. Phase stability in circular machines was established as a powerful new concept.

New Machines for New Physics

This was only the first step in a long series. Let us make up a little calendar of the wonderfully rapid progress in physics that was taking place at this time, and see how it fitted in with the invention of new machines that were to confirm and extend these discoveries. For a long time an important question had puzzled physicists. What holds the nucleus of an atom together? Here are positively charged particles, all crowded together, but like charges repel. Presumably the particles should be repelling each other most violently. Why does the nucleus not blow itself apart? Obviously, since nuclei do not explode, there must be some cement or binding force that holds the particles together. This binding is not evident when the particles are far apart. But let the particles get really close together, as in a nucleus, and then some powerful attraction must suddenly grab them and tie them together. What is the nature of this *nuclear* force?

Now we come to the story of a very imaginative and successful prediction, which at the same time has its humorous side, showing how some very acute prophecies can sometimes be misapplied. In 1935 the Japanese physicist H. Yukawa predicted that a certain new particle must exist to account for the properties of the nuclear binding force, and in particular for its limited range. He called his so far hypothetical particle the *meson,* the name (from Greek roots) implying that the mass of the particle would probably be intermediate between that of the light electron and that of the heavy proton. Within two years particles of approximately the predicted mass were indeed observed in cosmic radiation, the constant influx of high-energy particles that rain on the earth's atmosphere from outer space. It was very reasonably assumed that these mesons were the particles predicted by Yukawa, and that they would be the agents responsible for cementing the particles together so firmly in a nucleus. We had a beautiful example of man's power for predicting phenomena that never had been observed!

Slowly, however, this happy situation began to deteriorate. It was found that the cosmic-ray mesons exhibited few of the activities that would have been expected from a nuclear cement. For example, such a cement, almost by definition, must interact strongly with nuclear matter; the mesons did not. So began a period of casting around for new explanations for patching up the old theories. This painful process was fortunately brought to a stop when C. F. Powell, in 1948, discovered *another* kind of particle in cosmic rays. This one turned out to be the real McCoy, at last: it had all the properties expected of Yukawa's meson. It was christened the π-meson (pi-meson, or pion), and the older particle was called μ-meson (mu-meson, or muon). Once more peace reigned in this field of physics, and Yukawa's prediction was vindicated.

Note that these particles were discovered in cosmic radiation, and this indeed is an almost universal rule. By looking long enough and carefully enough at the constituents of this constant influx of particles, you can find almost anything that is known or expected to exist. The reason is that cosmic rays—mostly protons—arriving at the earth from outer space carry enormous energies at times, reaching 100 Bev (billion electron volts) and even higher. As these high-energy particles penetrate the earth's atmosphere, they interact violently with the nuclei of atoms they encounter. In the process, since such enormous energies are available, all kinds of particle creations can occur. It is just this process that we aim to duplicate in our super-high-energy accelerators. We would like to improve on nature, however. Our accelerators are to yield much larger numbers of particles than can be found in cosmic radiation. Then we can make much more precise studies, and control the conditions to suit our specific needs. Thus, although discoveries are often made in the already available cosmic rays, the detailed investigations usually have to wait upon the construction of suitable accelerators.

Now, how do the meson discoveries fit in the construction of accelerators, particularly of the synchrotron? The electron synchrotron was first established as a working machine around 1946, when the pion—the genuine cement particle—was still unknown. At that time, it was thought desirable to be able to create muons in the laboratory, and the only way that seemed possible was to make them in pairs, one positive and one negative. Physicists worked out how much energy would be needed to pay for the mass of the pair of particles that were to be created. A price of a little less than 300 Mev seemed right (cf. Appendix III). So several groups began construction of high-energy electron synchrotrons, each with a maximum energy somewhat above the 300-Mev mark. This was a determined bid for the creation of pairs of muons, but it need hardly be emphasized that at the same time many other experiments were envisaged for these machines.

The creation of muons in pairs has not been conclusively demonstrated yet in the laboratory, but no physicist doubts the possibility. It just happens to be a very difficult process. Moreover, physicists have found an extremely fertile field of research elsewhere. The discovery of the pion in 1948 revolutionized their thinking. At the same time, another contestant in the race toward higher-energy accelerators had entered the field

—the synchro-cyclotron. As it happened, it was this machine that was used for the first creation of pions in the laboratory.

The electron synchrotron, meanwhile, has found an important place in high-energy physics research. From the listing in Appendix IV, you can see that a number of higher-energy models have been constructed or planned since the original group of 300-Mev machines came into operation. As an example of these more modern machines, Plate XI shows the 1.3-Bev electron synchrotron constructed at Cornell University in 1954. The picture of the machine was taken during assembly, and none of the auxiliary apparatus is present to clutter the photograph. What you see is a slim, ring-shaped magnet—the guide field. Notice that it is not perfectly circular; there are four gaps, or straight sections, which are provided so that access to the orbit region becomes easier. This method of construction was first suggested by H. R. Crane, of the University of Michigan. His machine had two straight sections, and was for obvious reasons nicknamed the race track.

The illustration also gives an idea of the trend in modern high-energy accelerators. They grow bigger and bigger (the diameter of the electron synchrotron shown is about 30 feet), but at the same time refinements in guide technique permit the reduction of the bulk and weight of the machine. For example, the vacuum chamber of this synchrotron measures barely more than $1'' \times 3''$ in cross section!

Also visible on Plate XI is the injector which starts the electrons on their orbits. This one is a Van de Graaff machine operating at 2 Mv. It is enclosed in a high-pressure tank, which looks much like a boiler. To the designers of the synchrotron, the Van de Graaff injector seems just a small auxiliary. Only twenty years before, such a machine would have been regarded as a major triumph in its own right!

Appendix IV lists many other machines in the electron-synchrotron class. The largest are designed for an energy of about 6 Bev. To keep the significance of these energies in mind, you should refer to Appendix III from time to time. Here the mass-energy of the various particles is listed, so you can find the price in energy that has to be paid for creating them. In Chapter 9 we shall return to this point in greater detail, explaining in particular the creation of *anti-particles* and its significance. For the moment, let us summarize by stating what particles were created by the electron synchrotron of the various "generations": The original 300-Mev series could create pions in the laboratory and played an important part in untangling the detailed properties of this particle. The three machines designed for 1 Bev or a little more are able to make K-mesons in association with some of the hyperons. Finally, the two machines designed for around 6 Bev will be sufficiently energetic to create all the known particles and their anti-particles; this consideration in fact governed the choice of the design energy.

Chapter 8

THE SYNCHRO—CYCLOTRON

Appreciation of the synchrotron principle was not confined to the physicists interested in accelerating electrons. It was apparent that this was a powerful and versatile tool. Could it be used to improve the acceleration of protons?

Up to this point the cyclotron had been the principal proton accelerator, but the relativistic increase of the mass of protons as they reached about 20 or 30 Mev limited the energy. If experiments were to break through this relativistic barrier, the experimenters had to find another form of accelerator. The incentive was strong. The exciting discoveries following the Yukawa postulate had stirred up research.

One approach would be to accelerate protons in a linear accelerator, described in Chapter 4. No relativistic barrier exists here, and we need only make the machine long enough to attain any energy we care to demand. Of course, as the protons keep getting faster, the sections of accelerator must be longer and longer, and the machine will stretch the bounds of practicality. Except in very special circumstances, the idea seems altogether undesirable and inelegant.

The alternative was to think a little about the limitations of the conventional cyclotron. Lawrence had been doing that shortly before World War II and had proposed building a giant cyclotron with such a powerful accelerating voltage that it could overcome the relativistic barrier. Work on the giant was started early in the war. The magnet was to have a diameter of 184", more than *fifteen feet,* across its polefaces. The rest of the structure, coils and yoke, was correspondingly large and weighed thousands of tons. When the magnet was complete, pressure of the wartime programs for work on the atomic bomb became acute, and instead of a cyclotron, a giant magnetic separator for the isotopes of the element uranium was constructed.

Skirting the Relativistic Barrier

After the war, when the big magnet was free once more, the original cyclotron plans had received a great boost. By then the synchrotron principle had been discovered, and it offered a dazzling possibility for extending the operating range of the machine. To understand how this comes about, we must examine once more the limitations of the conventional cyclotron.

This machine has a constant guide field extending throughout a disk-shaped region. In this region protons (or other ions) accelerated by two RF electrodes travel in ever widening circles as their energy builds up. Although the circles get larger, the times of revolution of the protons do not get longer, because the ions move with correspondingly higher velocities on the longer orbits. Thus protons of widely different energies can be present at the same time in the cyclotron—on different orbits—and the same frequency of accelerating voltage can be used for them all. For this reason the conventional cyclotron is often called the fixed-frequency cyclotron.

It is easy to see that the cyclotron, in contrast to the pulsating machines, can act as a continuous accelerator. As fast as the ion source can put particles into tiny orbits at the center, the cyclotron will accelerate them toward the outside. It is also obvious that if the time of revolution in the machine should ever change, the fixed-frequency acceleration would no longer apply. This is what limits the cyclotron to energies of at most 20–30 Mev. Above these energies the mass of the protons begins to increase gradually; by the Theory of Relativity, if you put in energy, you are putting in mass also. So the protons begin to get appreciably heavier, and their times of revolution start to lengthen. Soon the particles drop out of step with the accelerating voltage and are lost.

If we wanted to accelerate protons above this limit set by Relativity, we would have to allow somehow for the slowing down of their revolutions. We could lower the frequency of the accelerating voltage, but then, of course, the lower frequency would no longer suit the original, low-energy protons in the center of the machine. To get out of this dilemma, we must establish a time sequence. So we begin the accelerating cycle at the usual, initial frequency. Then we lower the frequency progressively, and it becomes suitable for accelerating protons at higher and higher energies. But how can we hope to stay exactly in step with the particles all the way? We need not worry about this—the particles will have to stay in step with us! They have to obey the traffic policeman represented by the RF accelerating system.

The machine we have now designed works in a pulsating manner. Protons are accelerated in little bursts, each time the accelerating frequency is swung from the initial to the lower final value. (In practice, this action is repeated fairly fast, say between 30 and 300 times per second.) Naturally, a pulsating machine cannot achieve the same intensity as one working continuously, since it delivers output for only a small fraction of the time. But to offset this disadvantage, our machine can now accelerate particles to any energy we choose, limited only by the size and strength of the guide field. The giant 184″ magnet, for example, could accommodate the orbits of protons up to 350 Mev. It was with this machine that mesons first were artificially produced in 1948. The same magnet, later rebuilt for higher field strengths and a larger effective orbit space, can now reach up to proton energies of 730 Mev. This is a long, long reach beyond the limitations of the fixed-frequency cyclotron, and it has opened up a tremendous field of research in physics.

The improved cyclotron is called the synchro-cyclotron, because its practical realization depended on the synchrotron principle. It is also known as the frequency-modulated (FM) cyclotron; its accelerating frequency is swung, or modulated. After the spectacular success of the 184″ synchro-cyclotron at Berkeley, construction of several similar machines was undertaken (see Appendix IV). The knowledge we have obtained from these accelerators probably represents no less important an advance than followed the invention of Lawrence's original cyclotron. With the beams from the synchro-cyclotron, mesons in abundance can be created in the laboratory. All that is necessary is to allow the beam of protons circulating within the machine to strike a target mounted near the outer periphery. As the proton orbits expand, they will ultimately intercept this obstacle. High-energy protons interacting with the nuclei of the target, which can be made of many different substances, will cause the creation of pions and other disintegrations.

Figure 30 is a diagram of the synchro-cyclotron used

in this manner. Note that extraction of the circulating beam from the accelerator is unnecessary if an internal target can be used. When the interaction of the protons is to be studied outside the machine, the beam must be extracted, of course, and the figure indicates the method. From the *internal* target will emerge many kinds of particles, products of the interactions of the internal beam with the target nuclei. The neutral reaction products, such as neutrons and gamma rays, will emerge from the target and travel in straight lines, unaffected by the guide field of the machine. A charged particle, on the other hand, will be deflected by the guide field, and its trajectory will be curved until it has managed to escape from the field. Some particles, such as low-energy positive ones, may never manage this escape, and will be confined within the region of the guide field and ultimately strike the walls of the vacuum chamber.

Beams of Mesons

Also shown in Fig. 30 are the paths of some positively charged pions, and of negative ones. We see that positive pions can escape the guide field only if they leave the target in a backward direction. Negative pions, bent in the opposite direction, escape immediately upon traveling forward. Because of this difference, the positive pions available from the machine will be of lower energy: they are emitted *against* the direction of the original proton impact and thus do not carry the momentum represented by the bombardment. Since we can observe them coming off in the forward direction, the negative pions, by contrast, get the maximum benefit from the impact of the collision.

All the big synchro-cyclotrons have had standard arrangements fitted for observation of these external fluxes

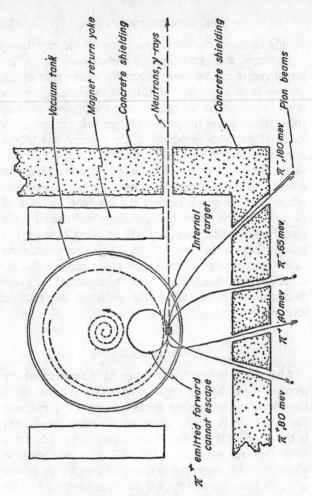

FIG. 30. *Use of a synchro-cyclotron with an internal target is illustrated here. Block of target material is placed near the outer circumference of vacuum tank, where accelerated protons will strike it as their orbits expand. Secondary particles from interactions of protons with target include neutrons, gamma rays, and positive and negative pions. Neutral particles emerge*

of mesons. The number of mesons created was so large that people started to talk of meson "beams," even though the mesons were not really the accelerated "beam" but merely debris from the interaction of the machine's beam with a target. The mesons leave through carefully located channels in the thick shield wall of the accelerator. On the outside of the shield, we see several little holes labeled, for example, π^+, 65 Mev, or π^-, 180 Mev. For reasons we have given, there are higher-energy "holes" for the negative pions than for the positive. You get an idea of how intimately the results of research are coupled with the properties of high-energy accelerators when you consider that, for a long time, the properties of negative pions were known up to much higher energies than those of positive ones!

As a result of a tremendous amount of research with these pion beams, the properties of this fascinating particle are now quite well understood. By this we mean that we know its mass, its "spin"—in layman's language, the rate at which it spins on its own axis—and its rather unusual symmetry properties. This last refers to parity. One could fill a book with talk about this important concept of parity, and you probably are aware that some quite revolutionary discoveries about parity were made in 1957 in experiments inspired by the daring theories of C. N. Yang and T. D. Lee, Nobel Prize winners in physics in 1957. Although the details are hard to explain, it comes down to a fairly familiar puzzle, which Alice explored when she entered the inverted world in *Through the Looking Glass*. This new Wonder-

---

through channel in shield wall in straight-ahead position. Negative particles, deflected outward by guide field of machine, emerge through other channels as shown. Positive pions, to escape guide field, must be emitted in backward direction and are consequently less energetic.

land greets us with scientific problems. Can you tell, once you have entered the looking-glass world, that it is not the real world? That its left hand should be its right hand? Or are all natural processes quite symmetrical? The answer is that you *can* tell.

But to return to our pion beams. Apart from the description of the pion, we have learned much about its life history. You see, pions are unstable particles, and they decay spontaneously only a very short time after they have been created—about two one-hundred-millionths of a second. Their decay product is none other than the muon, the particle which was first discovered and mistaken for the pion. Now we see how this happened.

Pions are created high in the atmosphere by the cosmic rays, but they decay rapidly and only very few manage to survive the long trip to the earth's surface. Instead, their decay products arrive down here. The muons, too, are very short-lived, but their decay takes considerably longer, perhaps two millionths of a second! Finally, when the muon has broken up, we are left with an electron. Whenever a pion is created, ultimately all traces of its existence disappear, leaving us only common, everyday particles. This is not altogether true, for a real cloak-and-dagger particle also is given off every time a pion or a muon decays. This mystery particle, the neutrino, leaves hardly any trace, however, for it has no mass and no electric charge. Nonetheless, its presence in the decay of the pion and of the muon gives rise to some startling phenomena connected with parity, and thus the synchro-cyclotrons have played an all-important role in the investigations concerning that concept.

Chapter 9

THE PROTON SYNCHROTRON

The success of the high-energy machines working on the synchrotron principle and the important body of knowledge gained from them sharpened the craving for accelerators of still higher energy. The work around the pi-meson is a good example of the mutual stimulation of theory and experiment in physics, of the supplementing of natural resources with tools. A similar cycle of discovery and investigation took place with the next generation of machines.

Again, the initiating discoveries came from observation of cosmic rays. Some strange and very rare events showing properties that could not be associated with any particles so far known had been observed. At first the evidence was very slight, but as more and more examples were brought to light, physicists became convinced that to the list of known elementary particles some newcomers would have to be added. Provisionally, these were nicknamed "strange particles," a name which has turned out to be quite long-lived. These particles had masses greater than that of the pion, but less than that of a proton. Later, other particles were discovered, with masses higher than that of the proton. Here then was a whole new batch of particles, but, as with the pion, a detailed investigation had to await the construction of sufficiently powerful accelerators to create the new-comers in the laboratory.

Anti-Matter

Apart from curiosity about the strange particles, an-other powerful motive was driving physicists to strive for extremely high energies. You will recall that besides the ordinary negative electrons, there are positive ones: these, as described in Chapter 1, can be created in the laboratory by high-energy gamma rays. The positive electron can be regarded as a sort of anti-electron: when it encounters the ordinary negative kind, the two can annihilate each other and release their combined mass-energy in the form of gamma rays. The British theoretical physicist P. A. M. Dirac had constructed a very elegant theory to explain the existence of these anti-electrons, and, in fact, his theory predicted that anti-particles should exist also for every other particle that is known. For example, there should be anti-protons. Given enough energy, one should be able to create an anti-proton, and later, this particle should be able to annihilate an ordinary proton and disappear again. This is a spectacular prediction, of course, for the amounts of energy involved in the case of the proton are huge—two thousand times more than for electrons.

Dirac's theory leads also to speculation that a com-plete world of anti-matter may exist somewhere, its atoms composed of anti-nuclei surrounded by anti-electrons. Such a world would be quite stable by itself; but let it encounter some ordinary matter and at once a tremendous orgy of annihilation would set in, all the anti-protons combining with protons, all the anti-electrons with ordinary electrons! So anti-matter would be short-lived and spectacular in a surrounding of ordinary matter; in the same way, ordinary matter penetrating into a universe of anti-matter would set off immediate fireworks. Keep the two kinds apart, however, and they could exist peacefully and almost without our being aware of any difference between them. Naturally, it would be an exciting thing for physicists to be able to create anti-protons themselves: these particles had never been observed.

The Cosmotron and the Bevatron

Therefore, hardly had the initial successes of the electron synchrotron and the synchro-cyclotron been reaped, when physicists set about studying the chances of reaching even higher energies. For the creation of strange particles, energies above one billion electron volts (1 Bev) would be needed; for creating anti-protons, as much as 6 Bev would be required. Now, of course the physicists could have gone on to build bigger synchro-cyclotrons to achieve these energies: no theoretical limitation stood in the way. But the orbit of a multi-Bev proton in the strongest magnetic field that can readily be achieved is enormous; it would be around 50 feet in radius, for example, at an energy of 6 Bev. To make a synchro-cyclotron for this energy, we would need a magnet with a solid poleface 100 feet in diameter! Not a pleasing prospect, and good reason for casting around for a better system.

The situation is more favorable if a ring-shaped guide field can be used, as was done in the electron synchrotron. Then we need only a narrow magnetic "channel" in which the particles can circulate, although of course the channel still must have a radius of 50 feet, or a circumference of more than 300 feet. Can one use the synchrotron principle for protons? The answer is yes—provided we pay some attention to the variation of the proton velocity during the acceleration cycle. In the electron synchrotron, you will remember, a great simplicity resulted from the fact that electrons reach almost the velocity of light at relatively low energies, and can thereafter be accelerated with a constant-frequency system. Protons, being so much heavier, approach the velocity of light only at much higher energies.

The proton synchrotron resembles the electron synchrotron in every respect, then, except that a constant accelerating frequency cannot be used. Instead, the frequency must be varied to keep in step with the increasing velocity of the protons as they acquire more energy. It is still true that the protons will be held in synchronism with the accelerating frequency by the action of phase stability, but we must make sure that the resulting orbit will have the right radius to fit into the machine. This involves calculation of the guide field at definite instants of time, and the frequency variation must be made to follow, or track, the variations of the guide field pretty accurately, or the particles will be forced off the desired orbit. In practice it is not too difficult to achieve this tracking. Some machines, indeed, have devices which automatically observe the orbit radius and adjust the accelerating frequency to suit!

By this time you will not be astonished to learn that the newly designed machines worked at once, and proved themselves valuable tools for just the kind of work for which they were intended. The first such large proton synchrotron was completed at the Brookhaven National Laboratory on Long Island in the late 1950s and is named the Cosmotron (Plate XIII). Its maximum energy is about 3 Bev, and, with the aid of its beam, experimenters have created all kinds of strange particles in the laboratory. Then, at Berkeley, an even larger accelerator was completed, the Bevatron (Plate XIV). Its energy is 6 Bev. With the Bevatron, the hope of creating anti-protons was finally fulfilled. These particles were soon discovered to exist, just as Dirac's theory had predicted, and their spectacular properties could be studied at will. A still larger machine than the Bevatron, with a peak energy of 10 Bev, was built in Russia. These giant machines represent enormous investments of money and time. Teams of hundreds of engineers and physicists must work many years before such a huge accelerator can be successfully put together, and the cost usually runs into many millions of dollars. The accelerator field, starting as a modest individual business, has in the short space of twenty years mushroomed into an enterprise of industrial proportions.

Speculations

Who finances these ambitious projects? And why trouble with such difficult research? As the scale grows, it becomes more and more true that only the largest laboratories, run as national institutions, can afford to compete in this field. Luckily, there has not been any lack of appreciation for the importance of fundamental research. It must be admitted that, as far as practical consequences are concerned, no immediate prospect of reward is evident from the investigation of strange particles or anti-matter. In the long run, of course, pure research has always been of practical benefit, too. But, here, the long run may be long indeed; the men holding the purse strings must be complimented on a very farsighted attitude. Or perhaps they are *interested* in physics? Is it possible for laymen to become excited about these remote problems?

For a physicist, it is hard to see how anyone can *not* become excited about the revolutionary discoveries that have followed on each other thick and fast. Just as an example, here is a story that may right now be about to "break"; it concerns that mysterious particle we have mentioned before, the neutrino. Ever since its existence was first proposed, the neutrino has had to lead a shadowy life. It carries no charge, has no mass, and interacts so weakly with matter that it is a major technological triumph just to detect its presence independently. (The neutrino was "invented" as an emergency measure to patch up what seemed to be a rather nasty failure of the conservation of energy principle in the radioactive beta decay of nuclei.)

In 1957 the neutrino was suddenly projected into the limelight, the experiments earning the Nobel Prize for the physicists C. N. Yang and T. D. Lee. Yang and Lee daringly had taken the neutrino's theoretical potentialities concerning parity at their face value. Now Lee has proposed that, maybe, the neutrino may not be such a retiring particle after all. His theory predicts that the interaction between neutrinos and nuclei may become very much stronger at very high energies. Now such neutrinos result when a high-energy pion or muon decays in flight; consequently there is speculation about the possibility of producing "beams" of high-energy neutrinos with the help of giant accelerators. The 30-Bev proton synchrotron recently brought into operation at CERN (see Chapter 10), and the similar accelerator close to completion at Brookhaven, might well be used in these experiments. The possibility of discovering a strong interaction of the hitherto so passive neutrino is one of the challenges of today's high-energy physics.

Chapter 10

FOCUSING

In the last few chapters we have seen how the discovery of a new principle—phase stability for circular machines—led to the rapid development of new types of accelerators and how the development kept in step with the discovery and laboratory investigation of new particles. Now we turn in a different direction to new work aimed at reducing the cost and effort of building the huge guide fields of the accelerators.

The function of the guide field, as outlined at the end of Chapter 6, is not only to bend the particle paths into closed orbits for repeated accelerations with the same electrode system. The guide field also must correct small deviations of the particles from their expected orbit—it must act as a sort of automatic navigator. This navigating we describe as focusing, and we can see its problems if we compare the guide field with a long pipe and imagine trying to look down the pipe. For illustration suppose we consider a periscope.

Acceptance of a Pipe

Figure 31 shows a periscope in an elementary form, a mirror at the top, one at the bottom, and a long

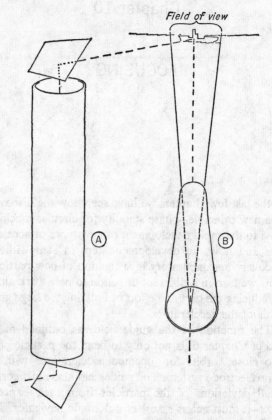

FIG. 31. *The apparatus at A is a simple periscope. Light from the object strikes the mirror, is reflected straight down the tube to another mirror, where it is reflected to the observer's eye. If the mirrors are removed, as at B, the observer could see the object by looking through the tube directly at it; this illustrates the restriction of his field of view caused by the tube.*

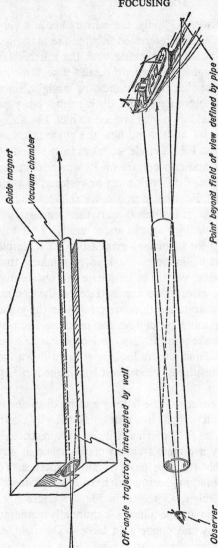

FIG. 32. This diagram compares the guide field of an accelerator and a long, straight pipe, taken from the periscope of Fig. 31. To emphasize the points of similarity with the periscope's tube, imagine the accelerator as cut open and straightened out. In both cases, the usable aperture is limited by the diameter of the tube in relation to its length.

straight pipe between. Plainly, the mirrors act in a very simple fashion. We are interested in what the long pipe will do to our vision. Dispensing with the mirrors for the moment, imagine looking down the pipe directly. We notice at once that the pipe must be straight, since light travels in straight lines. This distinguishes our pipe from the guide field of a synchrotron, which lies along a circle. By now we understand how the guide field can bend particles into such a circle, so let us forget bending for the moment and concentrate on its other function: particles that wander off orbit must be restored to their proper positions. For this purpose we might think of the guide field as straightened out; then comparison with the periscope pipe comes more easily. (All this may seem like a lot of mental gymnastics for a simple comparison; but it illustrates the kind of thinking that is useful in science. We try to eliminate the unessential from a problem in order to concentrate on the central question.) To recapitulate then, we straighten the guide field out in our mind by cutting the machine open at one place and unbending it. The periscope has had its mirrors removed, and we are looking straight down the long pipe. The resulting comparison is sketched in Fig. 32.

Now if the periscope pipe is long and its diameter is small, the amount of light that can go all the way down is very small. Our *field of view* will be very restricted; we can see only a minute fraction of the scene at any time. We say that the pipe has a small acceptance. To improve this situation, periscopes have a set of lenses built into their tubes, as shown in Fig. 33. Here light going at an angle to the pipe is continually gathered together again by the converging lenses. The field of view becomes much larger, the pipe has a larger acceptance. The lenses do just what we expect from the focusing action of the guide field: they restore deviating

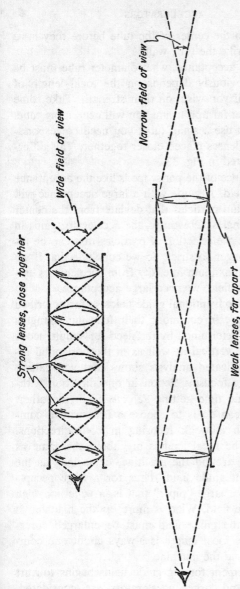

FIG. 33. If we place a series of converging lenses inside the straight tube of the periscope, we can enlarge the field of view. The lenses keep gathering the light before the diverging rays can strike the wall of the tube. The stronger the lenses—that is, the shorter their focal length—the wider will be the resulting field of view. If, with weak lenses, we wished to increase the field of view, we would have to use a pipe of larger diameter.

rays of light to the center of the tube before they have a chance to strike the tube wall.

For a given acceptance, what diameter tube must be used? This obviously depends on the focal length of the lenses or, if you wish, on their strength. Take some weak lenses, set far apart, and you will need a big tube. If you want to use a small tube, you need correspondingly stronger lenses placed closer together. This difference is illustrated in Fig. 33.

The acceptance of the periscope is like the acceptance of our guide field. A guide with a large acceptance will accept and retain particles that deviate from the center line by large angles. Obviously, the accelerator gains in intensity, since the selection of particles that can be retained is no longer so strict. So we conclude that if we are to get the maximum intensity from accelerators employing a guide field, we need large acceptance.

Now all the conventional guide fields so far described have one feature in common: their focusing strengths are fairly well determined by the need for simultaneous focusing in the vertical as well as in the horizontal directions. Complicated analysis shows that you cannot obtain a strong focusing action in one direction without at the same time getting *defocusing* in the other. The best you can do is to choose a field with a compromise, which is weak focusing in both directions. How weak? The focal lengths are about the same as one revolution around the machine, or as long as the straightened-out guide field. Thus for a large acceptance, we need a large "pipe," that is, a *wide* and *high* region of guide field. What is more, as the machine is made bigger, the guide field must be enlarged correspondingly; the focal length is always about one complete turn around the machine.

This requirement for big guide fields begins to hurt when larger and larger accelerators are considered.

There comes a point when we no longer can afford to pay for the necessary huge magnets; on the other hand, the penalty for making them smaller would be reduced intensity of the resultant beam of particles. This reduction makes experiments slower and more inaccurate.

Alternating-Gradient Focusing

In 1952, physicists from CERN were interested in multi-Bev machines and visited Brookhaven to study the Cosmotron. (CERN stands for Conseil Européen pour la Recherche Nucléaire, an inter-European co-operative organization with headquarters in Geneva, Switzerland. It was founded to permit the smaller nations to collaborate in the costly and complex high-energy projects. The existence of such an organization and its successful operations show the importance attached to high-energy physics research by the various governments. An entirely similar organization, formed for the benefit of the nations in the Soviet bloc, has been set up at Dubna in the U.S.S.R.) The European physicists began to plan a 10-Bev accelerator which would resemble the Cosmotron. They decided on a design using many magnet sections. The advice they asked of the Brookhaven physicists concerning this scheme actually led to the invention of a new design principle for magnetic guide fields by Ernest Courant, of Brookhaven, Hartland Snyder, of Brookhaven, and Livingston, who, you will recall, worked with Lawrence.

Courant, Snyder, and Livingston's idea was this: We cannot obtain strong focusing in the vertical direction, for example, without getting defocusing horizontally, and this seems an insuperable obstacle. But suppose we alternate sections of guide field which focus strongly first in one direction, then in the other? We then would get in both directions a succession of strongly focusing

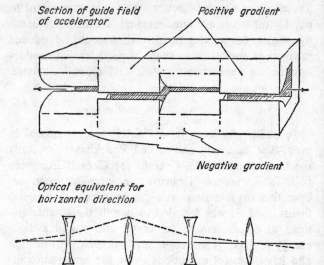

Section of guide field of accelerator

Positive gradient

Negative gradient

Optical equivalent for horizontal direction

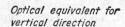

Optical equivalent for vertical direction

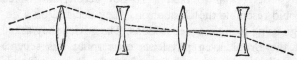

FIG. 34. *Alternating-gradient focusing is compared here with the action of a sequence of converging and diverging lenses. The section of the guide field shown at the top of the diagram has magnets of different pole-face contours that give fields that increase or decrease radially. The equivalent optical lenses for the two directions of deviation of a particle are shown below.*

and strongly defocusing lenses, as illustrated in Fig. 34. The trick is to choose just the right lengths of sections. Then the defocusing pieces are actually overpowered by the focusing ones, and the over-all effect turns out to be fairly strong focusing, in both directions! The comparable result in our periscope pipe would be obtained if we had to build in some *diverging* lenses to pay for the use of strongly convergent ones. There again, a succession of converging and diverging lenses has an over-all converging effect, provided the lenses are properly spaced.

This system of "switchback" focusing is called alternating-gradient focusing. The *gradient* of the magnetic field describes the change of field along the radius from the center of our machine. If the field is constant, the gradient is zero. If the field decreases as we move toward the outside, the gradient is negative, and if the field increases toward the outside, the gradient is positive. A large positive gradient gives strong horizontal focusing, while a large negative gradient focuses vertically. To summarize all these facts, then: an alternating-gradient accelerator has a guide field composed of many sections, in which the field alternately increases and decreases toward the outside of the machine.

The new system of focusing had some limitations, however, which originally escaped the attention of the Brookhaven physicists. It was the Europeans who afterward discovered these finer points. Thus by exchange of ideas on a large international scale the new principles were finally completely worked out—a good example of the benefits that this kind of close contact can bestow.

The advantages of the new system are very important when very high-energy accelerators are considered. As an example, we might think of a proton synchrotron with a maximum energy of 30 Bev. The orbit diameter for such a machine is 650 feet! If we used conventional, or weak, focusing we would need a guide field of very large cross section, perhaps 5 feet high by 10 feet wide. Alternating-gradient focusing cuts down on these re-

quirements spectacularly. Now the guide field need only
be about 3 inches high by 6 inches wide. You can visualize the magnet as a very slim unit, then, stretching
around a circle of very large diameter. The whole aspect of these machines has been changed, therefore, and
we can begin to think realistically in terms of such high-
energy accelerators. In fact, people have done more than
think about them: several such devices are well advanced in construction. One of them—the 30-Bev synchrotron at CERN—was put into operation successfully
in November 1959, and with a beam of 10^{10} protons
per pulse. Plate XV gives an idea of this giant machine.
The 30-Bev machine at Brookhaven National Laboratory was scheduled to be completed in 1960. There is no
predicting, of course, what further discoveries these accelerators will bring us, but one thing seems certain.
The drive to achieve higher energies will not soon
diminish.

To Greater Intensity

There is another direction in which accelerators can
be expected to develop, and are in fact already developing on drawing boards and in model construction. This
is the drive toward higher intensity of the accelerated
beams of particles. Evidently, it is the *energy* of the beam
that determines whether a certain type of event, such
as particle creation, can or cannot occur. Just having
enough energy to establish the possibility, however, is
not enough. We must also have sufficient intensity to
make the event acceptably *probable*.

Some experiments have been envisaged in which,
with present accelerators, one of the desired type of
events might be observed every year. Whether such an
experiment is feasible is a very doubtful point. For one
thing, it may not be possible to tie up a big accelerator

exclusively for one experiment for a whole year. Again, the apparatus for the experiment may be so complicated and delicate that it cannot be expected to function correctly for such a long period. Finally, and most important, to observe the event just once or twice may not be enough. Perhaps information must be abstracted from many events to detect trends in the reaction that cannot be determined from a single example. Then the experimenter would be in serious trouble indeed if he had to accumulate a total of one hundred events! It is evident, therefore, that intensity sets a practical limit on the possibility of certain experiments.

All the modern accelerators we have talked about are pulsating machines. Their output would be much greater if they could function continuously instead of just in brief spurts, but two conditions must be satisfied before an accelerator can work continuously. The guide field must be fixed, and the accelerating frequency must be steady. Both these conditions exist in the conventional cyclotron, which is the only steady-current accelerator among the circular machines we have described.

When we considered extending the energy range of the cyclotron (Chapter 8), we suggested decreasing the frequency of the accelerating voltage. Then it could accommodate the lower speeds of revolution as the particles started to become heavier. This is the operating principle of the synchro-cyclotron. Another approach would have been to make the guide field stronger toward the outside of the machine. The higher-energy particles, traveling farther out, would feel stronger bending forces and would travel on relatively smaller orbits. This can be arranged to compensate for their increased mass; the accelerating frequency can then be kept constant, and so it will suit particles of all the energies at once. Why was this scheme not adopted? Back in 1938, H. A. Bethe and M. E. Rose had pointed out that a field that increases as we move away from the center of the machine has a *defocusing* action in the vertical direction and cannot be used in an accelerator. As soon as any particle deviates ever so slightly from the central plane, the defocusing action would drive it farther away and finally force it into the walls of the vacuum chamber. L. H. Thomas at the same time had pointed out a method of overcoming this defocusing action. His suggestion, however, fell into oblivion, probably because accelerator techniques were not then sufficiently advanced to embody it easily. Further, most physicists did not completely understand the power of his scheme. Today, after rediscovering the principles Thomas foresaw, we realize how advanced his thinking was.

Now we have learned already how to deal with defocusing fields—intersperse them with focusing fields placed at suitable intervals. This same approach works for the constant-frequency cyclotron. By putting suitable alternating-gradient sectors into this machine, we can arrange to avoid the vertical defocusing effect while still correcting for the increased mass of the particles at the higher energies. The alternating-gradient sectors extend all the way from the center of the machine to the outside, and have to be carefully calculated so that they produce the required combined effects. In practice, they consist of ridges on the poles of the magnet, either in the radial direction or spiraling outward in gentle curves.

This technique of designing fixed-field accelerators has been labeled FFAG (fixed-field alternating-gradient) and is credited to Keith Symon of the Midwestern Universities Research Association. There are many other applications of the FFAG principle. We can make not only fixed-frequency cyclotrons that work at very high energies, and betatrons with a much improved beam intensity, but also FFAG synchrotrons, and even machines in which two beams of particles can simultaneously be accelerated in opposite directions around the guide field! Such devices promise great new fields of research to the physicist, quite apart from the quest for increased intensity that motivated the original idea.

To return to this intensity question, however, let us see what sort of performance one might expect from a FFAG cyclotron with a maximum energy of 500 Mev. It is not unreasonable to expect a beam of current of at least 1 milliamp—this is the sort of beam encountered during the pulse of existing synchro-cyclotrons. Here, though, the milliamp would be present at all times, instead of the short bursts repeated perhaps 100 times per second. A beam of 1 ma at 500 Mev represents an electrical *power* of 500 kilowatts. Compare this with an ordinary 100-watt light bulb—the beam power is equivalent to 5000 such light bulbs. When this beam strikes some target, all this energy must somehow be dissipated. Most of it, of course, will appear as heat. Unless the target is very efficiently cooled, the heat will melt it at once. At this power level the output of nuclear radiations will become important on a practical scale. The target will radiate, among other things, neutrons in about the same quantity as would be associated with an atomic pile operating at the same power level. It is well known what tremendous shielding such piles require. In the same way our FFAG cyclotron will demand enormous shielding walls around it, and will probably have to be situated far underground. Should it ever break down, it would be impossible to repair its inner components immediately; they undoubtedly would have become highly radioactive from the high-intensity bombardment. Probably this would mean that remote-handling equipment would have to be provided for such a machine.

Chapter 11

SYNCHROCLASH

The dynamics of the bombarding particle and its target impose a serious limitation on the useful energy of conventional accelerators. The limitation concerns the amount of energy that is actually available to produce the reactions we want.

When a high-energy ion from an accelerator strikes a stationary target particle, part of the energy goes into moving the target, and is wasted. It is as if we were trying to break a stone by hitting it with a hammer. To see what we are trying to get at, let us consider a few examples of this process. To the extent that the hammer blow simply moves the stone, the energy is not available for breaking it. Now if the hammer is very light and the stone very heavy, we can see that the target will not move very far; almost all the energy of the hammer will go into breaking or chipping the stone. If we use a heavy sledge on a light pebble, most of the energy goes into moving the stone, and very little of it is available for breaking the stone. If the hammer and stone weigh the same, they will tend to move off together with half the speed of the incoming hammer; exactly half the energy will be available for breaking the stone.

It is the same with atom smashing. But here Relativity plays a low trick, robbing us of most of the advantage to be gained by increasing the energy of the bombarding particles. We have already seen that when a particle attains a really high energy then there is a corresponding increase in its mass. Thus as we go up in energy, we increase the weight of our "hammer" and in a collision with another particle a larger and larger fraction of its energy becomes unavailable. At 1 Bev a proton is already noticeably heavier than when it is at rest; when it hits a stationary proton, 57 per cent of the energy is wasted and only .43 Bev is available for useful purposes. At 3 Bev (the energy of the Brookhaven Cosmotron), the available portion is 1.15 Bev; at 6 Bev (the Berkeley Bevatron) the available portion is 2 Bev; at 10 Bev, 2.9 Bev are available; at 50 Bev, 7.5; at 100 Bev, 10.5. We see that increasing the energy 100 times, from 1 to 100 Bev, results in only a 20-fold actual gain in the energy that can be used for study.

Solution by Head-on Collision

Suppose, however, that instead of firing a moving particle at a stationary one, we arrange a head-on collision between two high-energy particles. Then the mass increase is symmetrical, and upon collision there is no tendency for the colliding particles to move one way or the other. All the energy of both is now available for the desired reactions.

The physicists at the Midwestern Universities Research Association have seriously proposed such an experiment. They have designed a machine in which two beams of protons traveling in opposite directions (Fig. 35) are accelerated to 15 Bev in the same machine. The beams intersect every so often and here head-on collision can occur. This type of accelerator has been called synchroclash. The name speaks for itself. In the collisions 30 Bev is available. This is to be compared with the 6 Bev that would be available if a 15-Bev proton were incident on a proton at rest. In fact, to attain a useful energy of 30 Bev in an ordinary way would require at least 500 Bev.

Why should it be necessary to emphasize that a proposal of this sort is *serious?* You must realize, first of

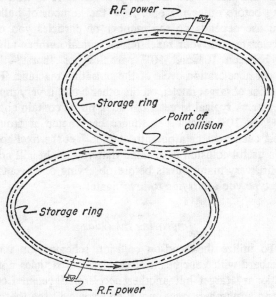

FIG. 35. *In the colliding-beam experiment, diagramed here, two intersecting storage rings using constant magnetic guide fields are first "filled" with high-energy electrons from a linear accelerator. The beams are maintained against radiation losses by small radio-frequency "accelerating" electrodes. If other losses can be kept low, the beams will continue to circulate for hours, and experimenters can observe head-on electron-electron collisions at the point of intersection.*

all, that bombarding any nucleus with fast particles is a very unrewarding business if you look at it from the viewpoint of good marksmanship. You fire your bullets at random into the target, and since the nuclei occupy such a minute fraction of the space, it is very rare to score a good hit. In other words, you need very large numbers of bullets, and you must make them strike thick targets containing very many nuclei. Otherwise, your hits will be so rare that you will have to wait too long before observing one. Now the number of bullets you use depends on the number of particles you can accelerate with your machine. A typical number might lie between 10^8 and 10^{12} particles per "burst"—that is, per acceleration cycle of the pulsating machine. The number of target nuclei, on the other hand, is very much greater. A typical target 1 cm thick might contain about 10^{22} or 10^{23} nuclei per square centimeter of frontal area, each nucleus a potential target. Yet the likelihood of a useful collision is so small that you might still need to fire very many bursts before observing one event of the type you are trying to investigate!

Improving the Odds

To utilize the head-on collision scheme, you must bombard with your beam of accelerated particles not a stationary target but another *accelerated beam*. Look over the numbers once more, and you will see that no accelerated beam so far obtained even remotely approaches the number of target nuclei that you can obtain in a stationary chunk of matter. The intensity of our beams falls far, far short of the one required to make the head-on collisions an even remotely feasible scheme. The physicists at MURA have proposed some rather clever tricks for improving the odds. What they are planning to do is to hoard up the accelerated beams so that the intensity of the final, circulating beam will be the accumulated result of many individual acceleration cycles. This sort of process is called *beam stacking*. Of course, a beam-stacking accelerator has to be a very special breed of machine. The act of accelerating another burst of particles, usually called "bringing up a bucket," must not disturb the stacked beam circulating at high energy, and the high-energy stack must be well protected from all sources of accidental loss. A great effort of thinking and calculation has gone into these schemes to spot and bypass the many possible pitfalls.

A variant has been proposed by G. F. O'Neill of Princeton. He will separate the accelerating and storage portions of his setup and thus be able to use existing accelerators and concern himself only with the storage problems. His program is already well along the road to completion. Using the Stanford linear accelerator as a source of electrons at about 200 Mev, O'Neill expects to store large amounts of the electron beam in a guide field in the shape of a figure eight. Each loop of the guide field is really a small electron synchrotron, but the magnetic field is fixed, since the particles are not expected to gain energy; the radio-frequency "accelerating" system is reduced to the secondary function of making up for the small loss in energy which the electrons suffer due to synchrotron radiation.

If all goes well, the operation of this scheme will be extremely elegant. First, we inject high-energy electrons into the loops, filling them gradually until the highest possible density of electrons has been reached. After this, the linac will no longer be required, since the guides are expected to store electrons for several hours without appreciable loss. The electron beams sit quietly bombarding each other at the point of intersection, and the experimenters can stand by to observe electron-

electron collisions at very high effective energies—400 Mev. A conventional electron synchrotron or linac would need to reach an energy of 40 Bev to give equivalent information about electrons colliding with electrons.

Chapter 12

COSMIC ACCELERATORS

If the description of man-made particle accelerators has tended to be boastful, then a look at what nature can do might put our human efforts in a less flattering perspective. Somewhere, somehow, out in space is a really giant accelerator which produces fantastic energies—as much as a billion Bev. Its products are the cosmic rays that have already been mentioned so frequently in this book. Cosmic radiation has been the subject of intensive study ever since its discovery over fifty years ago. We cannot concern ourselves here with the full story, which is long and exciting in itself, but photographic plates, cloud chambers, and ionization chambers sent up to great heights in balloons (100,000 ft.) and rockets (to the moon and beyond), together with studies at the surface of the earth, have given us much information about the nature of the radiation incident on our atmosphere. In summary you can think of the earth as being bombarded from all sides—primarily by very high-speed protons (77.5 per cent), ions of helium (20 per cent), ions of lithium, beryllium, boron (1 per cent), ions of carbon, nitrogen, oxygen (1 per cent), and by ions of all elements of higher atomic number (about 0.5 per cent altogether). The composition of this radiation is, in fact, about the same as the relative abundance of elements on earth, in meteorites, in the solar and stellar atmospheres (as determined by spectroscopic analysis), and even in interstellar matter (as revealed by the absorption of light). The protons have various energies: There are more at low energies than at high, but the average is high, about 5 Bev, and an occasional proton comes in with an energy of 10^{10} Bev.

The Origin of Cosmic Radiation

Such high-energy particles, on the top of our atmosphere, make collisions with the nuclei of the atoms of the air. The result is that the nuclei are completely shattered and many mesons produced. The resulting fragments and mesons share the energy of the incident proton, and even their energies are tremendous. They in turn make further collisions. A great cascade multiplication or showering occurs, and by the time the "shower" reaches the surface of the earth it may be comprised of as many as 10^{10} particles. Were our eyes more sensitive, we would see this most beautiful natural phenomenon as we looked heavenward. We would see a dense reddish-purple light emanating from the air in the core of such a shower and extending from the ground to the top of the atmosphere; around this core would be a thinner luminosity that would reach out with diminishing intensity to some hundreds of meters. It is by measuring the numbers of particles in such showers at the earth's surface, using a variety of particle detectors, that we can determine the energy of the primary particle.

It is not known exactly how these energetic cosmic-ray particles are produced, but we do have some quite plausible ideas of some possible mechanisms for the cosmic accelerators. Enrico Fermi suggested that the acceleration of ions is due to their collisions with regions in the galaxy containing magnetic fields. We picture intergalactic space as being filled with great clouds of ionized gas that may have been shot out of stars. You are doubtlessly familiar with the spectacular phenomena that can be observed near the surface of the sun during an eclipse. Violent motions occur and great prominences can be seen to extend out from the sun. In the course of these motions great volumes of plasma—that is, gas which is almost completely ionized—are thrown off into space. Because the ionization of the plasma causes it to act like a perfect conductor, any magnetic field that exists in the plasma when it is thrown off is trapped and travels with the plasma.

Collision with Plasmoids

These clouds of plasma and magnetic field, sometimes called plasmoids, float through space as definite objects and make collisions with one another. When such plasmoids come past the earth, magnetic storms and radio blackouts occur as well as huge fluctuations in the number of cosmic rays that reach the earth's surface. On the average, the magnetic field in the plasmoids has a strength of about 10^{-6} to 10^{-5} gauss. (The earth's own magnetic field is almost 1 gauss.) We can visualize these plasmoids as moving in all interstellar space and colliding constantly with one another.

Now if an ion falls into one of these objects, the magnetic field causes a curvature and, although the magnetic field is very small, still the size of the plasmoids is so large that the ion is deflected through 180° and so back out of the plasmoid: it is reflected. But, as we know, when a tiny mass makes an elastic collision and is reflected from a large moving object, then after the collision the speed of the small mass is increased; hence it gains energy. (Think of a slowly moving ball being struck by a massive bat.) A principle of physics called the principle of equipartition tells us that when we have bodies of different mass making random collisions, the kinetic energy of all the individual bodies tends to become the same on the average. Thus the individual ions that make collisions with the plasmoids will tend to acquire as much energy as the whole plasmoid. Now the energy of the plasmoids is tremendous, and equilibrium with the ions is probably never quite established for lack of time, or we would see cosmic rays of even larger energies. The ions gain their energy as they travel about in space in random motion. They make countless collisions with plasmoids throughout their lifetime, which can be thousands or millions of years. Eventually, they are lost out of the galaxy or make collisions with cosmic dust.

Fermi worked all this out in an elegant mathematical manner and found many points of agreement with actual observations of the characteristics of cosmic rays. There are still some difficulties with various details of the theory—but perhaps satellites as well as rockets out in space will give us the detailed knowledge of plasmoids and ions in space that will be necessary to provide a detailed theory of this fascinating phenomenon.

In any case, perhaps it is salutary for the nuclear physicist with his paltry tens of Bev to feel humble before this huge generator giving energies a billion times larger, or maybe, in his arrogance, he will just consider this another challenge. Time alone will tell.

CONCLUSION

As remarkable as the accelerators themselves, perhaps, is the social phenomenon that such large and expensive devices are constructed at all. Expenditures of over 100 million dollars are not trivial by any standard. We might very well ask why it is that various nations have provided the monies for such projects. Now, in the energy up to about 20 Mev—the cyclotron region—and perhaps even up to 100 Mev, we are clearly concerned with nuclear properties. There is no doubt about the eventual practicality of nuclear energy as a source of power. The military applications, alas, have only too well been demonstrated. In fact, nuclear weapons almost dominate the world power politics of today, and though we may lament this situation, we need not look very far for strong sociological or political reasons for constructing cyclotrons or some synchro-cyclotrons—even apart from the deep and aesthetic satisfaction that comes from adding to our understanding of nature. There is no doubt that some of the post-World War II impetus for building cyclotrons has come from the association of atomic bombs and atom busters—the feeling that military security depends on supremacy in the field of nuclear physics.

But when we come to the energy region above, say, 100 Mev, the picture changes. Now we are investigating the nature of neutrons and protons themselves. It is not at all obvious that this is a directly useful activity. There is no indication or evidence that great stores of energy are locked within the proton or neutron. When "strange particles" or mesons are created in the course of our high-energy bombardments, they have been manufactured at the expense of the energy put into the accelerated beam. High-energy physics is quite comparable to astronomy where one has seen no "practical" applications after the problem of navigation was solved. On the other hand, both sciences have been particularly rewarding in the dramatic extension of our knowledge of the deep secrets of nature—the knowledge of the kind that man seeks not merely to comprehend what is "out there" or "in there," but in order to understand himself. Furthermore, scientific knowledge has always become useful in the long run. How can we know now what the world of fifty years hence will be like?

The optimistic view of all this is, then, that men of affairs in many nations understand these deep strivings for knowledge and are motivated by such considerations in supplying the financial aid that is necessary for progress. If so, we can justifiably be proud that mankind has developed to a point where it takes such an enlightened view of pure research in such an as yet impractical field. This was not true a few decades ago and now it seems to be happening in countries of the most diverse political philosophies—in Russia, Great Britain, China, France, Brazil, as well as the United States.

But perhaps other considerations are also involved. Are statesmen misassociating high-energy physics and military might? We hope they are not. Still, national prestige seems to be an important consideration in these tumultuous times when some kind of struggle for the minds of men is going on. Scientific prowess is an important index to the level of cultural life of any country, and the cultural level is one of the most important factors in winning respect and friends. So in a struggle between competing political systems, it may well become necessary for each system to demonstrate that science flourishes under it. We can count ourselves fortunate indeed if future conflicts resolve themselves on the high plane of this kind of cultural competition. Perhaps scientific achievement is being demonstrated by the various governments when they support the development of particle accelerators.

The expenditures for scientific machinery are, of course, still trivial compared with the total national budgets. We tend to take the optimistic point of view of all this. As long as there are challenging questions to be answered by building larger and larger accelerators, then men will pick up the challenge, even apart from nationalistic competition, and do whatever is necessary to obtain the answers.

APPENDIX I

UNITS OF MEASURE

Any measurement of a physical quantity must be expressed in terms of a fundamental unit relevant to that quantity. For example, we may express measurements of length in terms of inches or miles; time in seconds, hours, or years; weight in ounces, pounds, or tons. The units chosen are usually quite arbitrary; the criterion is *convenience*. The inch, for example, used to be defined as the width of the King's thumb. Nowadays, more permanent standards are set; carefully preserved metal bars define our units of length.

Scientific measurements are usually expressed in the *metric system,* which has the advantage over some of the other systems that its units are related to each other by even factors of ten, one hundred, etc. Conversion from one unit to another—say, from grams to metric tons—is thus much simpler than the corresponding conversion from ounces to tons. In the following table we have collected some of the metric units used in this book and given examples of their magnitudes.

TABLE I

Quantity	Metric Unit	Example
Length	Meter	One meter = about 40 inches, or just over one yard.
Weight	Gram	One ounce = 28.5 grams; a dime weighs about 2½ grams. (One metric ton = one million grams.)
Time	Second	We all have an idea of how long a second lasts!
Work, or energy	Joule	One joule is approximately the work done in carrying a book weighing 1½ pounds up one step of a staircase.
Power, or rate of work	Watt	One watt = one joule per second. A motor working at 20 horsepower is delivering about 15,000 watts; a 1000-watt electric kettle will bring a quart of cold water to the boil in about 6 minutes.
Electromotive force ("Voltage")	Volt	A single flashlight cell has a voltage of about 1.5 volts.
Charge	Coulomb	A fully charged car battery might be able to deliver a total charge of about 200,-000 coulombs before being completely run down.

Quantity	Metric Unit	Example
Current	Ampere	One ampere = one coulomb flowing per second. An ordinary light bulb takes about one ampere to light; the starter motor of a car might draw more than 100 amperes.
Magnetic field	Gauss	The magnetic field at the surface of the earth in the United States is a little less than one gauss. A powerful permanent magnet may have a field of several thousand gauss between its poletips; iron-cored electromagnets with fields of about 20,000 gauss have been constructed.

APPENDIX II

NOTES ON THE USE OF POWERS OF TEN

Since physical measurements are made over an enormous range of magnitudes, extremely small or extremely large numbers are often required to express the results in terms of a common unit. The wavelength of light, for example, is about 1/2,000,000 meter, or 0.000,000,5 meter, while the distance to the moon is about 300,000,-000 meters. These numbers become very cumbersome to write and handle: a shorthand system for expressing them has therefore been invented. The number 1000, for example, is written 10^3; $1,000,000 = 10^6$; $1,000,-000,000 = 10^9$. You notice that the small number written to the right of and above the ten (the *exponent*) expresses the number of zeros in the longhand version of the same number. (It is also the number of times *ten* has to be multiplied by itself to get the same result.) For numbers that are not such simple *powers of ten,* we use a similar system. First we break off the uneven factor, and then we express the round part as powers of ten. For example, $3,500,000 = 3.5 \times 1,000,000 = 3.5 \times 10^6$. In the same way, $125 = 1.25 \times 10^2$; $30,000 = 3 \times 10^4$; $5,789,000,000 = 5.789 \times 10^9$.

If we want to go to smaller powers of ten, an easy way of extending the system downward suggests itself. Thus $100 = 10^2$; $10 = 10^1$; $1 = 10^0$; now $0.1 = 10^{-1}$; $0.01 = 10^{-2}$. These *negative* exponents may seem strange at first, but their usefulness is impressive. Another way of introducing them would have been to write, first, $0.01 = 1/100$; then we have $1/100 = 1/(10^2)$; and now we can say that the negative exponent indicates *dividing* so many times by ten, rather than multiplying. Thus $10^{-2} = 1/(10^2)$. Let us write down a few more numbers with negative exponents: $0.000,001 = 1/1,000,000 = 1/(10^6) = 10^{-6}$; $0.000,1 = 10^{-4}$; $0.000,01 = 10^{-5}$; $0.05 = 5 \times 0.01 = 5 \times 10^{-2}$; $0.000,35 = 3.5 \times 10^{-4}$; $0.000,000,5 = 5 \times 10^{-7}$.

The usefulness of this shorthand is apparent when extreme numbers are concerned; for example, the electric charge of an electron is 1.6×10^{-19} coulomb, which in longhand would have been 0.000,000,000,000,000,-000,16 coulomb—quite impossible to decipher. Or the distance to the nearest star, about 4×10^{16} meters, would be 40,000,000,000,000,000 meters. More impressive still is the ease with which multiplication and division can be carried through in this notation. We just observe the rule that to multiply two powers of ten we *add the exponents;* to divide one power of ten by another, we *subtract* the second exponent from the first. Examples: $10^2 \times 10^3 = 10^5$; $10^5/10^3 = 10^2$; $10^{19}/10^{12} = 10^7$; $10^5/10^8 = 10^{-3}$; $10^2/10^{-3} = 10^5$; etc. For complete numbers, including an odd factor in front, proceed in the same way: $(3 \times 10^2) \times (2 \times 10^5) = 6 \times 10^7$; $(4 \times 10^1) \times (5 \times 10^7) = 20 \times 10^8 = 2 \times 10^9$; $(5 \times 10^3)/(2 \times 10^2) = 2.5 \times 10^1$.

Sometimes it is convenient to use a word or syllable to denote a unit that has been multiplied or divided by powers of ten. Thus geographical distances are rarely expressed in meters, but instead in terms of 10^3 meters or *kilo*meters. The prefix *kilo* denotes multiplication by 10^3, or 1000. The same prefix may be used with other units: we talk of *kilo*grams and *kilo*volts, each time meaning 10^3 grams or 10^3 volts. There exist several such prefixes, listed in the following table.

TABLE II

Prefix	Abbreviation	Meaning	Example
kilo	k	times one thousand (10^3)	One kilogram = 10^3 grams.
Mega	M	times one million (10^6)	One Megavolt = 10^6 volts.
Beva Giga	B G	times one billion (10^9)	One Bv (= one Gv) = 10^9 v. (In Europe, one *billion* means 10^{12}, so that the term *Giga* is substituted for *Beva* over there.)
centi	c	divide by one hundred (times 10^{-2})	One centimeter = 0.01 meter.
milli	m	divide by one thousand (times 10^{-3})	One millimeter = 10^{-3} meter.
micro	μ	divide by one million (times 10^{-6})	One microvolt = 10^{-6} volt.
nano	n	divide by one billion (times 10^{-9})	One nanosecond = 10^{-9} second.

You can make up your own units by combining any prefix with any unit.

APPENDIX III

A. *Particles Used in Accelerators*

The particles we wish to accelerate must be electrically charged—if we are to have a "handle" with which to exert a force on them. Accelerators so far have used only *stable* particles, that is, those which do not decay spontaneously; the important groups are (1) electrons and (2) ions.

The *electron* is a constituent of every atom. It is the carrier of negative electricity. Its mass (m) and its electric charge (e) are so tiny that it is impossible to visualize them; to set the scale, these two quantities are often used as the *units* in terms of which the mass and charge of other particles are expressed. It turns out that all charged particles carry exactly the same amount of charge as the electron, but the sign of the charge can be either the same or opposite. The mass of the electron can also be stated by giving its *energy equivalent;* this is 0.51 Mev.

Ions are atoms in which the balance of electric charge has been upset, either by adding or by taking away some electrons. Negative ions (atoms with *excess* electrons) are rarely used in accelerators, except in the tandem Van de Graaff machines (Chapter 3). Positive ions of various elements have been accelerated. The most important is the hydrogen ion, which you will recognize as the *proton*. The proton's mass is 1836 m, and its charge is $+e$. In terms of energy, the proton mass corresponds to 938 Mev, or almost a billion electron volts.

A close relative of the proton is the *neutron;* this is very slightly heavier (1839 m, or 939 Mev), and it has no electric charge. Hence it cannot be accelerated directly, which is a pity, since many important questions involve the use of neutrons as well as protons. High-energy neutrons can be made indirectly by bombarding targets containing them with other high-energy particles. The most useful missile for this purpose is the ion of heavy hydrogen, or deuterium. This ion is called the *deuteron;* it consists of a proton and a neutron bound fairly loosely together. The resulting unit has electric charge, because of the presence of the proton, and the neutron, much like a passenger, is accelerated alongside. Ions of still heavier atoms have also been used in accelerators, but their application is much less general.

B. *Other Particles*

Energy in electromagnetic waves is not distributed uniformly, but appears in discrete packets. These have all the properties of a particle; the names used are *photon, quantum, X-ray,* or *γ-ray*. A quantum has the intriguing property of having zero rest-mass; all its mass comes from its energy of motion. As a consequence, if a quantum is made to stop, it vanishes. High-energy quanta can be generated by allowing fast electrons to strike an obstacle, thus producing X-rays. Another particle with zero rest-mass is the *neutrino,* which is involved in the radioactive decay of particles. The neutrino participates in observable activity through this decay,

TABLE III

Symbol	Name of Particle	Electric Charge	Mass, relative to electron mass	Mass-energy (Mev)	Lifetime (seconds)	Decay Products
γ	Photon (quantum, X-ray, γ-ray)	0	0	0	Stable	—
ν	Neutrino	0	0	0	Stable	—
e	Electron	$(\pm)$	1	0.51	Stable	—
μ	Muon (Mu-meson)	$(\pm)$	207	106	2.2×10^{-6}	$e + \nu + \bar{\nu}$ ($\bar{\nu}$ indicates anti-neutrino)
π	Pion (Pi-meson)	$+ (-)$	273	140	2.6×10^{-8}	$\mu + \nu$
		0	264	135	below 10^{-15}	2γ
K	K-Meson	$+ (-)$	967	494	1.2×10^{-8}	complex, includes π, μ, e, ν, γ
		0	~ 967	~ 494	complex	complex
p	Proton	$+ (-)$	1836	938	Stable	—
n	Neutron	0	1839	939	10^3	$p + e + \bar{\nu}$
Λ, Σ, Ξ	Hyperons	± 0	2180–2590	1115–1320	$\sim 10^{-10}$	complex

which is a slow and improbable reaction. It is therefore very hard to detect neutrinos but not impossible.

Beyond the particles so far mentioned, there are several families of particles known as *muons, pions, K-mesons,* and *hyperons.* These are all unstable, usually with very short lifetimes, and they decay into other particles in various patterns. In Table III we have collected

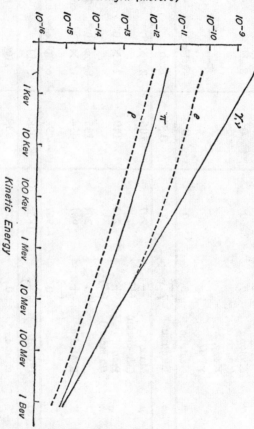

FIG. 36

the data for all these particles, making a rather impressive Who's Who. Perhaps the most important column, as far as accelerator physics is concerned, is the one giving the energy equivalent of the mass of each particle. This is the minimum energy which must be made available before such a particle can be created.

Beyond the particles in Table III, there is the complete group of their respective anti-particles (see Chapter 9). A few particles and their anti-particles are identical, but mostly they are different. The anti-particle of a charged particle carries the opposite sign of charge. (This is indicated in the table by writing the charge of the anti-particle in parentheses.) For example, the ordinary negative electron has an anti-particle with positive charge: the *positron*.

When particles are used as "light" with which to examine very fine details, their wavelength becomes of paramount importance. In Fig. 36 we have plotted the wavelengths of several particles as a function of their energy. By reading this graph, you can determine how high an energy is required to make the wavelength of a bombarding particle sufficiently short to reveal detail of interest.

APPENDIX IV

The interest in this field of physics is evident in the
large number of accelerators that have been constructed
all over the world. Many of them represent investments
of manpower and money that are serious strains on the
organization or country undertaking the work. A reli-
able listing of *all* accelerators has never been compiled,
and the numbers which follow are really only minimum
estimates.

First we list the population of machines by their species:

Type	In Opera-tion	In Construction or Design
Cyclotron	56	16
Synchro-cyclotron	18	0
Proton synchrotron	6	9
Electron synchrotron (energy above 0.5 Bev)	3	8
Betatron and low-energy electron synchrotron	Figures not available; estimate about 20	
Linac	10	7

Next, a list of accelerators according to the country in which they are situated:

Argentina	1	Denmark	1	Rumania	1
Australia	3	France	6	Sweden	4
Belgium	1	Germany	5	Switzerland	3
Bulgaria	1	Israel	1	Union of South	
Canada	2	Italy	1	Africa	1
China	1	Japan	6	U.S.S.R.	21
Czecho-		Netherlands	3	United Kingdom	10
slovakia	1	Poland	3	United States	56
				Yugoslavia	1

Finally, it might be interesting to group these accelerators by the energy they have achieved (or are expected to achieve):

Below 10 Mev	16
10–30 Mev	55
30–100 Mev	12
100 Mev–1 Bev	24
1 Bev–10 Bev	17
Above 10 Bev	8

The design energy was not known for all accelerators included in the previous two groupings, so that the total number in this last list is slightly lower. It must be emphasized again that the data on these accelerators are incomplete, and that some types—notably betatrons, low-energy synchrotrons using betatron injection, and all direct accelerators—have not been included at all.

BIBLIOGRAPHY

JAMES A. COLEMAN: *Relativity for the Layman,* Mentor book, New American Library, New York, 1958.

M. S. LIVINGSTON: *High-Energy Accelerators,* Interscience, New York, 1954.

—— and J. P. BLEWETT: *Particle Accelerators,* International Series—McGraw Hill, New York, 1961.

W. B. MANN: *The Cyclotron,* Wiley, New York, 1954.

R. R. WILSON: "Particle Accelerators," *Scientific American,* March 1958.

FRANCIS BITTER: *Magnets,* Science Study Series, Doubleday Anchor Books, Garden City, New York, 1959.

DONALD J. HUGHES: *The Neutron Story,* Science Study Series, 1959.

ALAN HOLDEN and PHYLIS SINGER: *Crystals and Crystal Growing,* Science Study Series, 1960.

ALFRED ROMER: *The Restless Atom,* Science Study Series, 1960.

INDEX

Accelerators:
  betatron, 103–16
  cosmic, 163–66
  cyclotron, 87–101
  early, 35–67
  electron synchrotron, 117–27
  linear, 69–85
  proton synchrotron, 137–42
  synchroclash, 157–62
  synchro-cyclotron, 129–36
  See also individual machines
Acceptance, 143–48
Akeley, L. E., and Lawrence, 12
Alpha rays, 50–51 ff., 97
  See also Helium atoms
Alternating current, 42–44 ff., 85
  in betatron, 106
  in cyclotron, 90 ff.
  in linear accelerators, 74, 78 ff.
  See also Frequencies
Alternating-gradient focusing, 149–52, 154–55
Alvarez, Luis, and proton linac, 85
Amber, Greeks and, 60
Anode, 37, 39, 44
Anti-matter, 14, 138–39, 141, 183
Anti-particles. See Anti-matter
Argentina, accelerator in, 186
Astronomy, high-energy physics and, 168
Atomic bombs, 32–33
Atomic piles, 155

Atoms, 21–22 ff., 46, 51, 123–24
  in crystals, 47
  helium, 50–51 ff.
  hydrogen, 28, 53. See also Hydrogen
  radioactive, 49
  and spectroscopy, 67
  See also Ions; Nuclei
Australia, accelerators in, 186
Automatic timing stability. See Phase stability
Automobiles, analogies with, 113, 118–20
  and speed of light, 79

Balls, analogies using, 71–73 ff., 115, 165–66
Barnes, D. E., and synchrotron, 122
Batteries, for high voltage, 41
Beams of particles, 55, 152–55
  extracted, 92–93, 94, 109, 133
  mesons, 133–36
  neutrinos, 142
  See also Cyclotron; Synchroclash; etc.
Becquerel, Henri, 49
Belgium, accelerator in, 186
Berkeley. See California, University of (Berkeley)
Beta rays, 50, 103 ff.
  See also Electrons
Betatron, 103–16, 185
  conversion of, 120, 122
  FFAG for, 154
Bethe, H. A., and focusing, 153

Bevatron, 14, 140–41, 158
Boat analogy, 23
Bobsled analogy, 113
Boron, in cosmic rays, 163
Bowling alley analogy, 71 ff.
Bragg, W. Lawrence, 47
Brookhaven National Laboratory:
CERN physicists at, 149 ff.
Cosmotron, 140, 158
30-Bev accelerator, 142, 152
Bulgaria, accelerator in, 186

California, University of (Berkeley), 85, 132, 140, 158
Lawrence at, 12, 14, 52, 98–101
California Institute of Technology, Lauritsen at, 52
Canada, accelerators in, 186
Capacitors, 55
Carbon, in cosmic rays, 163
Cathode, 37, 44, 56
Cavendish Laboratory, 13–14, 51, 59
CERN, 142, 149, 152
China, accelerator in, 186
Circular accelerators. See Bevatron; Cyclotron; Synchrotron; etc.
Cloud chamber, 51–52
Clouds in space, 165–66
Cockroft, J. D., 13–14, 52, 93
Cockroft-Walton machine, 13–14, 46, 52–59
Collisions:
in space, 164–66
in synchroclash, 158–62
Combs, and static electricity, 63
Condensers, 55
Condon, E. V., and nuclear bombardment, 52
Cornell University, electron synchrotron, 126
Cosmic rays, 30–31, 123–25, 136

composition, 163–66
"strange particles" in, 137
Cosmotron, 140, 149, 158
Courant, Ernest, and guide fields, 149
Crane, H. R., and guide fields, 126
Crystallography, X-ray and, 47
Current. See Alternating current; Voltages
Cyclotron, 13, 87–101, 153, 154
and betatron, 103 ff.
Bevatron, 14, 140–41, 158
number of, 185
See also Synchro-cyclotron
Czechoslovakia, accelerator in, 186

Denmark, accelerator in, 186
Deuterium, 180
Deuterons, 97, 180
Dirac, P. A. M., and antimatter, 138
Distances, expressing, 175 ff.
Drift, 78

Eclipses, 165
Edison, Thomas A., and thermionic emission, 36
Einstein's Theory of Relativity, 31–32 ff., 82 ff., 158
and cyclotron, 96–97, 98, 130 ff.
Electrically-charged particles. See Electrons; Ions; Protons; also Particles
Electricity, 37–39, 41–46
A.C. See Alternating current
cyclotron power vs. light bulbs, 155
reservoirs of, 55–56, 57
static, 60 ff.
See also Electrons, etc.; Voltages
Electrodes, 35 ff.
in cyclotron, 88 ff.

Electrodes (*cont'd*)
in linac, 78, 79, 83–84
in synchrotron, 120, 130
in Van de Graaf machine, 64, 66
Electromagnetic spectrum, 24
Electromagnets. *See* Magnets
Electron microscopes, 25–27
Electron synchrotron, 117–27, 185
Electron volt, 38
Electrons, 12, 25–26, 180, 181
anti-, 138
in atom, 12, 51, 53
beta rays, 50, 103
in betatron, 103–5 ff.
electrical charge, 176
in linac, 81–84, 85
in microscope, 25 ff.
pair creation, 33
in scattering experiments, 28
and speed limit, 82–83 ff.
and static electricity, 63
in synchroclash, 161–62
in synchrotron, 117–27
and "synchrotron radiation," 111–12, 161
in X-ray tube, 35 ff.
Electrostatic generator, Van de Graaf, 59–67
Energy:
and accelerated electrons, 28, 37–39, 81 ff., 104 ff., 120–21 ff. *See also* Electrons
and anti-matter, 138
on chart, 181
in cosmic rays, 164 ff.
and electron microscope, 27
for injection, 108
and intensity, 152 ff.
-mass equivalence, 31–34, 179, 181
and neutrinos, 142
price for particle creation, 34, 125, 139
for strange particles, 139
in synchroclash, 158 ff.

and synchrotron radiation, 111–12, 161
of Van de Graaf machine, 66–67
and voltage, 37–38. *See also* Voltages
of X-rays. *See* X-rays
See also high-energy accelerators; i.e., Cyclotron; etc.; Radiation
Equipartition, 166
Europe:
accelerators in, 186
nuclear research organization. *See* CERN
Extraction of particles, 92–93, 109, 133

Fermi, Enrico, and cosmic rays, 164, 166
FFAG, 154–55
Flashover (sparking), 55, 57–59, 64, 69
Fleming, James A., and thermionic emission, 36
Focusing, 112–16, 143–56
France, accelerators in, 186
Frequencies, 153
in cyclotron, 94–96, 130 ff.
and phase, 94–96
radar, 84
radio, 79, 80, 117 ff., 161
in synchrotron, 117 ff., 140
See also Alternating current
Frequency-modulated cyclotron. *See* Synchro-cyclotron

Gamma (γ) rays, 50, 180
and anti-electrons, 138
wavelengths of, 24, 25
See also X-rays
Gamow, George, and nuclear bombardment, 52
Gas:
in cyclotron, 92
as insulation, 59, 64
in space, 165–66

Geiger counters, 25–26, 41
General Electric Research Laboratory, 122
Generator, Van de Graaf, 59–67, 121, 126
Germany, accelerators in, 186
Goward, F. K., and synchrotron, 122
Gradient focusing, alternating, 149–52
Greeks, and static electricity, 60
Guide fields, 143 ff.
 in betatron, 104 ff., 110 ff.
 in cyclotron, 130, 139–40
 in proton synchrotron, 151–52
 See also Magnetic fields

Hair, and static electricity, 63
Hammer-and-stone analogy, 157–58
Hansen, W. W., and electron linac, 84, 85
Heat, in thermionic emission, 36–37
Helium atoms, 50–51 ff., 163
Hydrogen, 28–29 ff., 53 ff., 93, 180
 from nitrogen bombardment, 51
Hyperons, 181, 182

Illinois, University of, betatron at, 111
Injection of particles, 59, 92, 107–9
 See also Cockroft-Walton machine; etc.
Insulation, 59, 64
Ionization, 53
Ions, 12, 66, 92, 179–80
 in cosmic rays, 163, 164–65, 166
 hydrogen, 53 ff., 180
 in synchroclash, 157 ff.
 in synchro-cyclotron, 130, 131

See also Protons
Israel, accelerator in, 186
Italy, accelerator in, 186

Japan, accelerator in, 186

K-mesons, 127, 181, 182
Kerst, D. W., and betatron, 103, 111

Laue, Max von, 47
Lauritsen, C. C., and transformer, 52
Lawrence, Ernest O., 87–88, 93–94, 98–101
 background, 11–15
 and giant cyclotron, 130
Lee, T. D., 135, 142
Light:
 quantum energy of, 40
 and sight, 21 ff.
 speed of, and Relativity, 79, 82, 83
 sun deflects, 32
 wavelength of, 175
Light bulbs, and cyclotron power, 155
Lightning, 60
 and Urban experiments, 13, 52
Linear accelerators (linac), 69–85, 129, 161, 185
Lithium, in cosmic rays, 163
Livingston, M. Stanley, 93, 94, 149
Los Alamos Laboratory, McMillan at, 117

McMillan, E. M., and electron synchrotron, 117
Magnetic fields, 25
 in cyclotron, 88, 95
 guide fields. See Guide fields
 in space, 165
Magnets:
 in alternating-gradient focusing, 149, 152, 154
 in betatron, 104, 111

Magnets (*cont'd*)
in cyclotron, 88 ff., 99, 130, 132, 139
in electron microscope, 25
in transformer, 44
Marbles, and light, 29
Mass:
and accelerated electrons, 82–83
and accelerated protons, 97, 131, 158
-energy equivalence, 31–34, 179, 181
small, in collision, 165
Measurement, 171–77
Mesons, 14, 123–24 ff., 132, 164
beams of, 133–36
See also Muons (mu-mesons); Pions (pi-mesons)
Metric system, 171–77
Michigan, University of, H. R. Crane at, 126
Microscopes, 22–23, 24–27
Microwaves, 84, 85
Midwestern Universities Research Association, 154, 158, 160–61
Military security, 168
Moon, distance to, 175
Muons (mu-mesons), 124, 125, 136, 181, 182
MURA. *See* Midwestern Universities Research Association

Netherlands, accelerators in, 186
Neutrinos, 136, 142, 180–82
Neutrons, 133, 155, 180, 181
Nitrogen:
alpha ray bombardment, 51
in cosmic rays, 163
Nobel Prize, to Yang, Lee, 142
Nuclear physics:
financing of, 141–42, 167
importance of, 167–69
research organizations, 149

and spectroscopy, 67
See also Accelerators
Nuclei, 123–24
bombardment of, 27 ff., 160–61. *See also* Betatron; Cyclotron; etc.
in cosmic rays, 164
first artificial disintegrations, 46, 51, 52 ff., 93
and neutrinos, 142
in pair creation, 33
Numbers, in powers of ten, 175–77

Oil, accelerator insulation, 59
O'Neill, G. F., and beam stacking, 161
Orbital stability, 112–15
Orbits, particles in circular. *See* Betatron; Cyclotron; Synchrotron; etc.
Oscillations, betatron, 115
Oxygen:
in cosmic rays, 163
from nitrogen, 51

Pair creation, 33
Parity, 135–36, 142
Particles, 25–26, 34, 40, 179–83
in cosmic rays, 30–31, 123–25, 163–66
and intensity, 152 ff.
in linac, 77, 78 ff.
scattering experiments, 27
"strange," 137, 168
in synchroclash, 158–62
in synchrotron, 120–22
See also Electrons; Ions; Protons; etc.
Periscopes, focusing of, 143–48
Phase, 76
Phase stability:
and cyclotron, 94–95, 97
in linac, 75–77, 85
in synchrotron, 118–22, 140

Philips Co., Cockroft-Walton machine, 59
Photon, 180, 181
Physics, nuclear:
 financing of, 141–42, 167
 importance, 167–69
 research organizations, 149
 and spectroscopy, 67
 See also Accelerators
Pions (pi-mesons), 124, 125–26, 127, 181, 182
 beams of, 133–35, 136
 energy price, 34
Planck, Max, 40
Plasma in space, 165
Plasmoids, 165–66
Poland, accelerators in, 186
Positrons, 33, 183
Powell, C. F., and pion, 124
Power, nuclear, 167
Powers of ten, 175–77
Princeton University, 60, 161
Proton synchrotron, 137–42, 151, 185
Protons, 28 ff., 79, 158, 180, 181
 in Cockroft-Walton machine, 52 ff.
 in cosmic rays, 31, 124, 163, 164
 in cyclotron, 13, 88–90 ff., 130, 131
 in linac, 80–81, 85
 in synchroclash, 158–59
 in synchro-cyclotron, 129, 131–33
 in synchrotron, 137–42, 151
Pulse transformer, 109
Pulsed electron gun, 108–9
Pulsed operation, 80–81

Quantum, 40, 180, 181

Radar frequencies, 84
Radiation, 24–25 ff.
 in circular accelerators ("synchrotron"), 85, 111–12, 122, 161

for power, 155
from radioactive substances, 49–50 ff.
 Roentgen's, 39–40
 See also Light; X-rays; etc.; Cosmic rays; Electrons; etc.
Radiation Laboratory. See California, University of (Berkeley)
Radioactivity, 49–50, 52, 155
Radio-frequency accelerating system, 79, 80, 161
 in synchrotron, 117 ff.
Radios, portable, 41
Rectifiers, 46, 55 ff.
Relativity, Theory of, 31–32 ff., 82 ff., 158
 and cyclotron, 93–97, 98, 130 ff.
Research, pure, 168–69
Reservoirs of electric charge, 55 ff.
Resonance principle, 96
Resonators, 80
Roentgen, Konrad, 39
Rose (physicist), and focusing, 153
Rumania, accelerator in, 186
Russia, 149
 accelerators in, 141, 186
Rutherford, Ernest, 13, 14, 51–52

Scattering, 27–30
Security, military, 168
Seeing, 21–27
Shielding for FFAG cyclotron, 155
Snyder, Hartland, and guide fields, 149
Sparking (flashover), 55, 57–59, 64, 69
Spectroscopy, 67
Speed:
 and collision, 165–66
 and energy. See Energy
 See also Accelerators

Stability, orbital, 112–15
    phase. *See* Phase stability
Stacking, beam, 161
Stanford University, 84, 161
Stars, distance to, 176
Static electricity, 60 ff.
Steering of particles, 113–15
Steinbeck, M., and betatron, 103
Strange particles, 137, 139, 168
Sun:
    deflects light, 32
    eclipse phenomena, 165
Sweden, accelerators in, 186
Switzerland, accelerators in, 186
Symmetry and parity, 135–36
Symon, Keith, and FFAG, 154
Synchroclash, 157–62
Synchro-cyclotron, 129–36, 153, 185
Synchrotron:
    electron, 117–27, 185
    FFAG, 155
    proton, 137–42, 151, 185
    radiation, 111–12, 161

Television, electron guns for, 108
Theory of Relativity, 31–32 ff., 82 ff., 158
    and cyclotron, 96–97, 98, 130 ff.
Thermionic emission, 36–37
Thomas, L. H., and focusing, 154
Thomson, J. J., and atom, 50
Timing stability. *See* Phase stability
Traffic analogy, 118–20
Transformers, 42 ff., 52
    pulse, 109
    and rectifiers, 55 ff.
Tuned system, 80

Ultraviolet, in microscope, 24
Union of South Africa, accelerator in, 186

Union of Soviet Socialist Republics, 149
    accelerators in, 141, 186
United Kingdom, accelerators in, 186
United States, accelerators in, 186
Uranium, 33, 49
Urban, Dr. C., lightning experiment, 13, 52

Van de Graaf, Robert J., 60
Van de Graaf machine, 59–67, 121, 126
Veksler, V., and electron synchrotron, 117
Voltages, 37–39, 41–46
    in Cockroft-Walton machine, 55–59
    dangers of high, 13, 55, 57–59, 64, 69
    in electron gun, 109
    in Van de Graaf machine, 60 ff.
    See also Alternating current; Frequencies

Walton, E. T. S., 13–14, 52, 93
    See also Cockroft-Walton machine
Waveguide, 84
Wavelengths:
    of alpha rays, 51
    of light, 24
    and sight, 23–24 ff., 183
    of X-rays, 46
Waves:
    electrons as, 25–26
    and images, 23–25
    See also Radiation; X-rays; etc.
Wideröe, R., 69, 84–85, 87
Wilson, C. T. R., cloud chamber, 52
Wimshurst machine, 60

X-rays, 35–41, 46–47, 180, 181
    in betatron, 109–11

X-rays (*cont'd*)
  and marbles, 29
  in microscope, 25
  and pair creation, 33
  in rectifier, 56–57
  See also Gamma rays

Yale University, Lawrence at,
  12
Yang, C. N., 135, 142
Yugoslavia, accelerator in, 186
Yukawa, Hideki, and mesons,
  123–24

SCIENCE STUDY SERIES

BENADE, ARTHUR H.   Horns, Strings, and Harmony, S 11

BITTER, FRANCIS   Magnets: The Education of a Physicist, S 2

BONDI, HERMANN   The Universe at Large, S 14

BOYS, SIR CHARLES VERNON   Soap Bubbles and the Forces Which Mould Them, S 3

COHEN, I. BERNARD   The Birth of a New Physics, S 10

DAVID, JR., EDWARD E.; VAN BERGEIJK, WILLEM A.; and PIERCE, JOHN R.   Waves and the Ear, S 9

DUBOS, RENÉ   Pasteur and Modern Science, S 15

FINK, DONALD G., and LUTYENS, DAVID M.   The Physics of Television, S 8

GRIFFIN, DONALD R.   Echoes of Bats and Men, S 4

HOLDEN, ALAN, and SINGER, PHYLIS   Crystals and Crystal Growing, S 7

HUGHES, DONALD J.   The Neutron Story, S 1

HURLEY, PATRICK M.   How Old Is the Earth? S 5

JAFFE, BERNARD   Michelson and the Speed of Light, S 13

KOESTLER, ARTHUR   The Watershed: A Biography of Johannes Kepler, S 16

LITTAUER, RAPHAEL, and WILSON, ROBERT R.   Accelerators: Machines of Nuclear Physics, S 17

LUTYENS, DAVID M., and FINK, DONALD G.   The Physics of Television, S 8

PIERCE, JOHN R.; DAVID, JR., EDWARD E.; and VAN BERGEIJK, WILLEM A.   Waves and the Ear, S 9

ROMER, ALFRED   The Restless Atom, S 12

SINGER, PHYLIS, and HOLDEN, ALAN   Crystals and Crystal Growing, S 7

VAN BERGEIJK, WILLEM A.; PIERCE, JOHN R.; and DAVID, JR., EDWARD E.   Waves and the Ear, S 9

WILSON, ROBERT R., and LITTAUER, RAPHAEL   Accelerators: Machines of Nuclear Physics, S 17

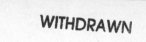